POCKET GUIDE TO

STARS
&
PLANETS

EDITOR: MARTIN WACE

CHANCELLOR
PRESS

Acknowledgements

References are to page numbers.
W. Cobley, Cleethorpes, 38 bottom; European Southern Observatory, 34
top; Peter Gill, London, 14; H.B. Ridley, West Chinnock, Somerset, 34
bottom; Royal Astronomical Society – Royal Greenwich Observatory,
16/17; Science Photo Library, London – US Naval Observatory, 118;
D.A.R. Simmons, Glasgow, 38 top.

Illustrations by David A. Hardy

Some of the material in this book previously
published in other Hamlyn books.

Cover photograph: © Frank Zullo / The Science Photo Library

First published in 1989 by The Hamlyn Publishing Group Limited

This 1998 edition published by Chancellor Press
an imprint of Reed Consumer Books Limited
Michelin House, 81 Fulham Road, London SW3 6RB

ISBN 0 75370 041 7

A CIP catalogue record for this book is available
at the British Library

Printed and bound in China

Produced by Toppan Printing Co., (H.K.) Ltd

Contents

Introduction

Astronomy can rightly be said to be the oldest of the sciences. Certainly early humans looked at the sky in awe and wonder, trying to understand what they saw. From these early beginnings, astronomy developed into the science it is today. It is a sobering thought that we are all descended from astronomers. But, ours is the first of the countless succeeding generations to begin to understand the universe and, maybe, ourselves.

This book introduces a number of aspects of astronomy, but the subject itself is so vast that it is impossible to cover any part of it in any real depth in a book of this size. Rather, it should be regarded as a 'taster' of one of the most fascinating and mind-stretching areas of modern science.

Up to about thirty years ago, astronomers were only able to explore the universe by using ground-based telescopes to make studies in light and radio waves, with which we are all familiar. Now things are very different. Astronomers can use Earth-orbiting satellites in addition to their ground-based instruments to view the universe across almost the entire spectrum, which stretches from long wavelength radio waves, through the microwave and infrared regions, through the optical (visible light), ultra-violet and X-ray portions, ending up in the regime of high energy gamma rays. This means that modern astronomy allows us to view the many different physical processes that are going on around us, from our upper atmosphere to the farthest reaches of the universe.

You may wonder what you can possibly do that would contribute to modern astronomy. After all, professional astronomers have big telescopes, powerful computers to help them analyse their observations, and satellite-borne telescopes to make observations unhindered by Earth's turbulent and cloudy atmosphere. The answer is that there is a great deal that can be done by the amateur with modest equipment. The fact of the matter is that the professionals simply do not have the time to observe everything and they rely heavily on amateurs to carry out a wide range of work. It is undeniably true that astronomy remains one of the few fields of modern science where the amateur, working in his or her back yard, can make a very real contribution. Indeed, it is often the case that comets and novae are discovered by amateurs before the professionals. Professional astronomers welcome, and in many cases actively encourage, amateur involvement. So, even if your eyes are the only optical equipment you possess, you will be able to carry out worthwhile observations.

Perhaps a few tips might not be unwelcome to new observers of the night sky. First of all, as most forms of astronomy are carried out at night, it will be desirable to dress warmly so that you remain comfortable and can concentrate on observing. It is a good idea to put on more layers of clothing than you think you will need. Your feet can become especially cold, so why not put on two pairs of socks. Do not be put off by the thought that you might get cold. Once you begin to notice the beauty of the night sky you'll just want to go on and on looking.

If you do decide that you want to begin making a real contribution, then you should record your observations in a book you keep specially for the purpose. It does not need to be a large book, but one with alternate lined and blank pages will do fine. Each time you make an observation, note the date and time as well as details of the object you observed. A pencil sketch will always be useful and will usually be better than a detailed written description.

Obviously it is going to be dark when you go out at night, but you should resist the temptation to take a bright flashlight with you. To get the most from the night sky, you will need to let your eyes adjust to the darkness for at least ten minutes. Remember that an ordinary flashlight will spoil your night vision. What you should really use is a dull red light. This will not spoil your night vision, and you will still be able to read your notes or this book.

Well, enough of the introduction with its do's and don'ts. You will find that astronomy is a very enjoyable, relaxing and rewarding way to spend your time. Even if you do not become a serious amateur astronomer, you will still get enormous pleasure from looking at the sheer beauty of what the night sky has to offer. So, if it is a clear sky tonight go ahead and introduce yourself to the universe. Perhaps you will get hooked and make a name for yourself amongst the 'astronomy greats'. Maybe you will have an enjoyable time. Either way, this book will have served its purpose.

Binoculars and telescopes

Although most amateurs do own some form of optical equipment, it is quite possible to enjoy observing with the naked eye alone, and a considerable amount of truly scientific work can be carried out in this way. Nevertheless there are obviously limitations, and anyone seriously interested in observational astronomy will want some form of instrument suitable for his or her requirements.

Binoculars

Binoculars are more versatile than a small telescope, and for many beginners in astronomy they are an ideal first instrument. If being chosen primarily with astronomy in mind, then a low magnification combined with a moderate-sized aperture is advisable to give maximum light-grasp and a fairly wide field of view. A pair of 7 × 50s (magnification 7 times, aperture 50 mm) enables stars down to at least eighth magnitude to be seen, and covers a field about $6\frac{1}{2}°$ in diameter. Such a pair can be used very satisfactorily for variable star work and for tracking artificial satellites.

Quite apart from these uses, binoculars are ideal for general sky sweeping. There is a lot to be said for undertaking a systematic survey of the constellations in order to familiarize oneself with the sky before concentrating on more specialized work. They are also useful for identifying the brighter double stars, clusters and nebulae. Finally, they can be invaluable as an auxiliary instrument for finding and identifying the fields to be examined with a larger telescope.

Any binoculars will give even better performance if they can be fitted to a mount of some manner. This is essential for the largest sizes. Wide-aperture binoculars are used by many workers who concentrate upon searching for comets and novae. The very largest apertures, 125–150 mm, are only available as ex-military equipment and are very rarely encountered. In any case, very few observers are proficient enough to be able to make proper use of them.

Telescopes

Some form of telescope is essential for most areas of serious observation. In amateur work the refractor and Newtonian reflector remain predominant, although the compact and relatively portable Schmidt-Cassegrain and Maksutov types are becoming increasingly popular, but these tend to be rather expensive. The minimum useful aperture is about 75 mm for a refractor and 150 mm for a reflector; smaller telescopes should be avoided in favour of a good pair of binoculars if you have a limited budget. Aperture for

Fig. 1 An altazimuth reflector of the type known as a Dobsonian is particularly easy to construct from ordinary materials.

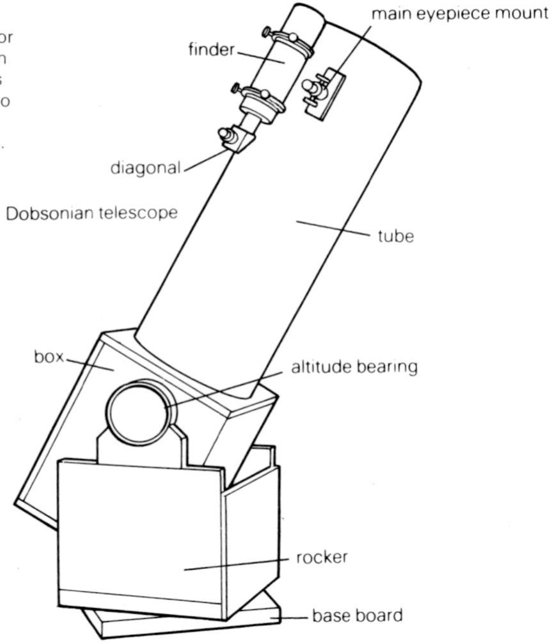

Dobsonian telescope

main eyepiece mount

finder

diagonal

tube

box

altitude bearing

rocker

base board

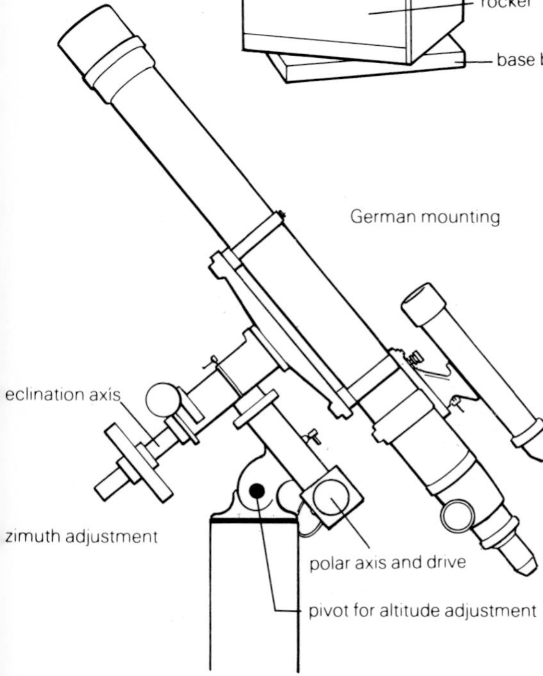

German mounting

eclination axis

zimuth adjustment

polar axis and drive

pivot for altitude adjustment

Fig. 2 The long focal ratios of most refractors make them very useful for solar work and, in the larger sizes, for double-star measurements and planetary observation.

7

aperture, 'ordinary' Newtonian reflectors are usually much cheaper than refractors or the compound types, and this is why they tend to predominate at the large sizes.

A 75 mm refractor is widely regarded as ideal for the beginner. It is sufficient to show considerable detail on the Moon, the belts of Jupiter, the rings of Saturn, countless double stars, clusters and nebulae, and can be used to advantage for observation of the Sun by one of the safe methods described on pages 12–17. However, if the observer is certain that his or her interests lie in areas where light-grasp is the most important consideration then a reflector might well be the best choice, especially as one of about 150 mm aperture would be comparable in cost to the 75 mm refractor. In the larger sizes, reflectors are usually the first choice, on the grounds of cost if nothing else. They may also be made of shorter focal lengths, and thus have 'faster' f-ratios than equivalent refractors: for this reason they are favoured for photographing nebulae and galaxies for example.

Cassegrain reflectors are particularly suitable for planetary work. Maksutov and Schmidt-Cassegrain types usually have long focal ratios (f/12 or more) and are best suited to examination of restricted fields such as planets. Maksutovs are particularly suitable for solar work **when a proper full-aperture filter is fitted**. Both of these types have become popular because of their portability.

Somewhere in between binoculars and the usual form of telescopes come the types described as 'comet-seekers' or 'rich-field telescopes'. Such equipment is frequently used, along with large binoculars, for comet and nova searching, and may consist of short-focus reflectors as well as specially designed and manufactured achromatic refractors with fast focal ratios.

Telescope-making is a very popular branch of amateur astronomy. Even for those with little mechanical aptitude, it is well worth considering the purchase of the finished optical parts for a Newtonian reflector, and constructing a simple, wooden tube and mounting for them. Such an instrument offers good results at reasonable cost. Objectives for refractors may also be purchased, but mounting these requires a greater degree of engineering skill than is needed for the mirrors in a reflector.

Mountings, observatories and accessories

There has been a move recently for reflectors to be mounted in simple altazimuth mountings – particularly in the so-called 'Dobsonian' mount – and this design is worth consideration by any beginner for its simplicity and cheapness. It has some advantages over other altazimuth designs when fast movement from one

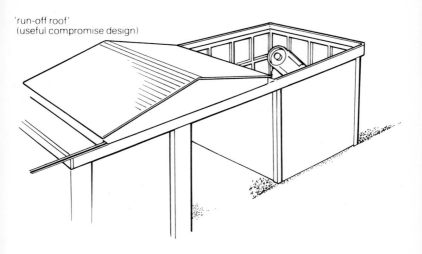

'run-off roof'
(useful compromise design)

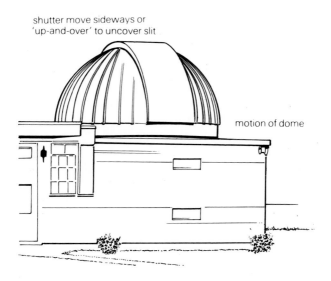

shutter move sideways or
'up-and-over' to uncover slit

motion of dome

Fig. 3 Amateur observatories may range from reasonably simple ones, such as those where the roof moves out of the way when in use (top), to proper domes (below) which give full protection to both telescope and observer at all times.

portion of the sky to another might be required. However, most serious observers will require a proper equatorial mount which can be easily driven to follow the sidereal motion, as well as allowing the use of setting circles. The portable Maksutov and Schmidt-Cassegrain instruments usually offer these facilities, but with refractors and reflectors a fixed permanent mount is desirable.

There are many different forms of mounting which may be used, but that known as the German mount is one of the best for refractors, while the Fork mounting is particularly suitable for reflectors and is the type most frequently chosen for Maksutovs and Schmidt-Cassegrains.

A permanently mounted telescope obviously needs to be housed in an observatory. However, even the portable forms require a firm base, and, more important, the observer will benefit from the protection – especially from cold winds – afforded by a proper observatory. There are many advantages to having an observatory, such as having everything to hand when observing.

Amateur observatories come in all shapes and sizes, from simple sheds to fully rotating domes. Perhaps one type which deserves wider use is that with a 'run-off' roof: this is basically four walls covered by a roof which is rolled back out of the way when the equipment is to be used.

It is now quite common for equatorially mounted telescopes to be provided with an electric variable-speed drive for motion in right ascension, together with a similar drive in declination. Some amateurs link microcomputers to their telescopes to give complete control in both axes. Such sophistication can also provide for push-button setting of the telescope on to the required object, in addition to the digital position readout. However, it should not be forgotten that all this electronic gadgetry is of little value unless it, and the telescope, is properly used. Many of the most accomplished amateur observers may be found using binoculars or simple telescopes without drives or setting circles. As always, it is the experience of the observer, not the equipment, which is all-important.

Various pieces of auxiliary equipment can be mounted on the main telescope. Common items are wide- and narrow-field finder telescopes, and a long-focus instrument of some form for use as a guide telescope when the main instrument is being used for photography. Cameras may even be attached to the mount, thus benefiting from the accurate drive.

The most essential accessories for any telescope are the eyepieces, and there are many different types which can be used. One of the simpler and more common types is the Kellner. More highly corrected, more complex and more expensive eyepieces of the Orthoscopic and Plösl types are popular for high magnifications, with Erfle and König forms finding favour for wide fields. It is important that the lenses used in eyepieces should be provided with anti-reflection coatings, as otherwise the light losses can be considerable. For the beginner, three eyepieces are normally sufficient: a low power for general work, a medium power for observation of the Moon and planets, and a high power for use when the turbulence of the atmosphere permits. A Barlow lens, which increases the magnification of a set of eyepieces, is also very useful – especially for lunar and planetary work.

Cameras used on the telescope are usually in the form of a standard SLR body mounted at the prime focus. Some observers go to the trouble of manufacturing special cameras for plates or sheet film.

It is worth emphasizing again that astronomy is one of the few sciences where not only can a great deal of enjoyment be gained, but also a serious contribution to knowledge may be made with only the very simplest of equipment.

Care and adjustments

You should always treat your telescope or binoculars with respect. They do not respond well to being knocked about – this is more true of reflectors, but you should treat any optical equipment with care. Unless binoculars or refracting telescopes have been severely mistreated there should never be any need for the optical elements to be adjusted. However, from time to time, the mirrors in reflecting telescopes will need to be removed for cleaning or recoating with aluminium. Cleaning the mirrors may be just a simple matter of gently blowing dust and other small debris from the delicate optical surfaces, but it might be that you will encounter more stubborn contamination. If this is the case, then you should seek professional assistance, perhaps from the same company that offers mirror re-aluminizing services or better still, from a company that makes astronomical mirrors.

If you have had to remove refractor or binocular lenses for any reason, all you need to do is to replace them in their proper position. There should be no need for further adjustment and observing can recommence almost immediately. The same is sadly not true of reflectors. The mirrors have to be realigned accurately if the instrument is to perform properly. This can be a fairly lengthy procedure, but it is not too difficult. When you have achieved the task once, you will know how to do it again next time.

Observing the Sun

It is most important always to bear in mind that **the Sun should never be looked at through binoculars or a telescope**. The disc is so bright and hot that permanent blindness would result if it were directly observed. Even prolonged staring at the Sun with the naked eye can damage the sensitive retina. The dark 'Sun filters' supplied with some telescopes **are not safe** and should never be used. They have been known to crack under concentrated solar heat in a telescope. Even when the Sun is low on the horizon, at sunrise and sunset, its infrared radiation may still be sufficiently great for it to be dangerous to use any optical equipment.

The Sun may be studied in perfect safety by adopting proper methods or by using special equipment. The simplest means is to project the solar image on to a white screen, preferably using a proper projection box mounted on the telescope as illustrated on page 12: by preventing stray light from entering the box the details can easily be seen. This method can be used with any telescope, even with binoculars. It is important to cover the objective of any finder on a telescope, or the other half of the binoculars, to avoid any possibility of an accident. The shadow of the telescope itself can be used to determine the pointing direction.

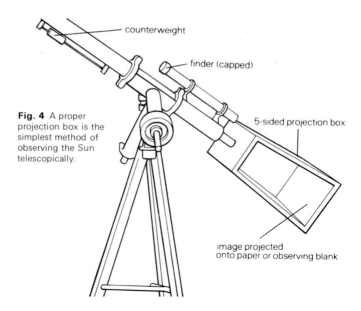

counterweight

finder (capped)

5-sided projection box

Fig. 4 A proper projection box is the simplest method of observing the Sun telescopically.

image projected onto paper or observing blank

Fig. 5 The large sunspot of 20 May 1972, drawn by Harold Hill over the period 06.45 to 07.10 UT, using a 75 mm objective.

Of the special equipment used for observing the Sun brief mention may be made of the Herschel wedge. This reduces the intensity by a factor of between 10^3 and 10^4 – still not enough for safe viewing without proper filters or other devices, such as specially prepared, uncoated mirrors which reduce the amount of light and heat. The intense heat of the Sun imposes a limitation on the size of telescope that can be successfully used, and those of 150 mm aperture or more should have the objective stopped down.

The greatest success and safety in direct viewing is achieved by the use of special reflecting solar filters. These consist of glass, or more commonly Mylar plastic film, coated with chromium or aluminium to reflect away the unwanted light and heat, passing only a small fraction into the telescope. As they are used over the objective, the whole telescope remains cool, a great advantage; and furthermore, quite large apertures may be used with the consequent gain in resolution. The coated film, which is somewhat similar to the thermal blankets used on spacecraft, **must be of the correct type**; suppliers will be given by organizations which coordinate the study of the Sun.

Apart from examining the Sun in white light, many amateurs study its features in the light of a single spectral line, usually Hα at 6536 Å, either by using special, and expensive, filters or by means of a complex instrument known as a spectrohelioscope. Basically, this spreads the light into a spectrum and then uses a second slit to reject all light except one narrow spectral band. Spectrohelioscopes have the advantage over filters that they can be used to examine any spectral region, not just one, as well as the fact that they do not require accurate temperature control, which must be strictly observed in the case of filters.

The simplest and most obvious form of observation is to note or draw the distribution of sunspots on the solar disc. If the projection method is used it is simple to plot the positions of any sunspots or faculae on a suitable sheet of paper. It is usual to arrange for the magnification provided by the optical train to be such that a standard-sized blank can be used, with a fixed solar diameter. Made on a daily basis, such disc drawings allow the evolution of individual sunspot groups to be followed, and the adoption of a standard diameter means that records from different observers may be easily compared.

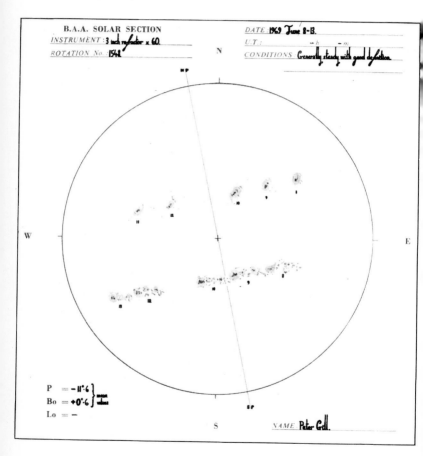

Fig. 6 A composite drawing from observations made using the equipment shown which shows the day-to-day changes in structure of two large sunspot groups that were visible during the first half of June 1969.

An assessment of the level of sunspot activity can be competently made by the amateur and is usually expressed in terms of the Zürich relative sunspot number R, which is derived from the formula $R = k(f + 10g)$, where g represents the number of sunspot groups, f the total number of their component spots, and k is constant which depends upon the estimated efficiency of a particular observer and the equipment he uses.

Sunspot numbers change in an 11-year cycle, and occasionally there may be none visible. They frequently appear in pairs (actually linked by magnetic fields) and active areas may consist of many individual sunspots. The solar rotation, which is faster at the equator than at the poles, carries the features across the disc from day to day. Although most individual spots do not last long, some may persist for more than one solar rotation (about 27 days), especially if they form part of a large active area. The projection method allows the number of sunspots and active areas to be followed easily. During the sunspot cycle the main centres of activity gradually migrate towards the equator, before beginning again at high latitudes.

Under good conditions granulation may be seen on the solar surface, together with larger bright areas (faculae), more easily seen towards the limbs. During a total solar eclipse large, glowing prominences may be visible around the limb where material is moving towards, or away from, the surface.

Hydrogen-alpha observations allow many fine details to be recorded, such as prominences (called filaments when seen against the disc), plages and sunspots. Flares are also more readily seen than in white light, and should be fully recorded.

Detailed structure is best recorded by photography, either in white light or in a narrow spectral band, and whole-disc photographs are a useful record of solar activity. Once again, when attempting white-light photography, precautions must be taken to ensure that the shutter of the camera, and the observer's eye, are not subjected to the concentrated heat of the primary image.

There is also the possibility of making radio observations. Some observers monitor the Sun for activity throughout the day, every day, using nothing more than a good communications receiver and a small Yagi aerial driven to track the Sun. Such equipment can be connected to a suitable chart recorder to give a permanent trace of the activity, and also arranged to provide an automatic warning when a flare occurs. Any such records can be correlated with those of other observers, and also with subsequent auroral activity. As an extension of this general field many amateurs are now observing and recording the changes in the Earth's magnetic field which occur with solar activity and auroral displays.

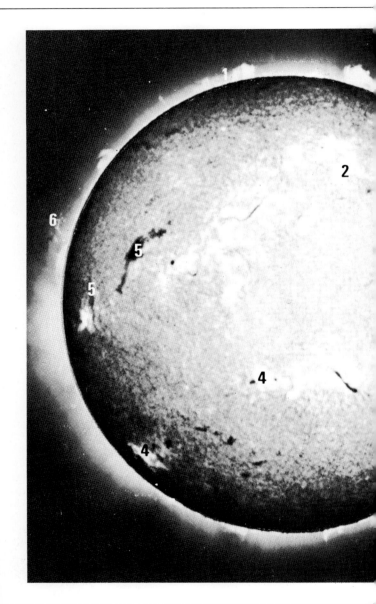

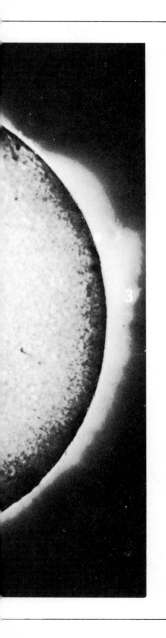

Fig. 7 A composite of a photograph taken in the Hα line of ionized hydrogen, superimposed on a white-light photograph of the corona. Faculae in white light are similar to plages (shown here).
1. quiescent prominence; **2.** hydrogen − α plage; **3.** coronal plumes; **4.** sunspot groups; **5.** filaments; **6.** active prominence.

The Moon's features

With a maximum magnitude of -12.7, the Moon has an observed average angular diameter of $31.09'$, compared with the Sun's angular diameter of $31.98'$, and sidereal and synodic periods of 27 days 7 h 43 min and 29 days 12 h 44 min respectively. Observation of particular features is usually undertaken during the phases when the terminator, the line separating lit and unlit portions, moves across the feature of interest. The low angle of illumination casts prominent shadows that accentuate the undulating surface. Prominent features suitable for observation can be found in the maps (see pages 20–27).

The Moon lies at a mean distance of 3.84×10^5 km from the Earth, and exhibits synchronous rotation, always presenting the same hemisphere to the observer. However, the Moon appears to rock, allowing additional areas in latitude and longitude to become visible from Earth at different times. In total up to 59 per cent of the surface can be seen due to this effect which is known as libration.

Since the Moon's orbit lies at an angle of $5.15°$ to the ecliptic, occultations of the Sun and Moon (eclipses) are only possible if conjunction and opposition respectively occur at the intersection of the two planes. The Sun's corona can only be observed during a total solar eclipse due to the near equality of the two angular diameters. At other times, when the Moon is waxing or waning, reflected Earth light dimly illuminates the dark side of the hemisphere facing the Earth.

Index to moon maps

Feature	Map	Position		Feature	Map	Position	
Albategnius	4	12°S	4°E	Fra Mauro	3	6°S	17°W
Alphonsus	3	13°S	3°W	Fracastorius	4	21°S	33°E
Archimedes	1	30°N	4°W	Gassendi	3	18°S	40°W
Ariadaeus Rille	2	7°N	11°E	Gauss	2	36°N	80°E
Aristarchus	1	24°N	48°W	Geminus	2	35°N	57°E
Aristillus	2	34°N	1°E	Grimaldi	3	6°S	68°W
Aristoteles	2	50°N	18°E	Hadley Rille	1	25°N	3°W
Arzachel	3	18°S	2°W	Hevelius	1	2°N	67°W
Bullialdus	3	21°S	22°W	Hipparchus	4	6°S	5°E
Clavius	3	58°S	14°W	Hyginus Rille	2	8°N	7°E
Cleomedes	2	27°N	55°E	Janssen	4	46°S	40°E
Copernicus	1	10°N	20°W	Julius Caesar	2	9°N	15°E
Darwin	3	20°S	69°W	Kepler	1	8°N	38°W
Eddington	1	22°N	72°W	Langrenus	4	9°S	61°E
Eratosthenes	1	15°N	11°W	Maginus	3	50°S	6°W
Eudoxus	2	44°N	16°E	Mairan	1	42°N	43°W
Firmicus	2	7°N	64°E	Manilius	2	15°N	9°E

Feature	Map	Position		Feature	Map	Position	
Mare Australe (Southern Sea)	4	37°S	89°E	Montes Haemus (Haemus Mountains)	2	20°N	8°E
Mare Crisium (Sea of Crises)	2	15°N	60°E	Montes Harbinger (Harbinger Mountains)	1	28°N	41°W
Mare Fecunditatis (Sea of Fertility)	4	5°S	50°E	Montes Jura (Jura Mountains)	1	45°N	37°W
Mare Frigoris (Sea of Cold)	2	50°N	35°E	Montes Pyrenaeus (Pyrenees Mountains)	4	15°S	43°E
Mare Humboldtianum (Humboldt's Sea)	2	57°N	83°E	Neper	2	7°N	83°E
Mare Humorum (Sea of Moisture)	3	24°S	40°W	Oceanus Procellarum (Ocean of Storms)	1	30°N	60°W
Mare Imbrium (Sea of Rains)	1	30°N	15°W	Piccolomini	4	30°S	32°E
Mare Nectaris (Sea of Nectar)	4	15°S	35°E	Plato	1	51°N	9°W
Mare Nubium (Sea of Clouds)	3	20°S	14°W	Plinius	2	15°N	24°E
Mare Orientale (Eastern Sea)	3	20°S	89°W	Posidonius	2	32°N	30°E
Mare Serenitatis (Sea of Serenity)	2	25°N	15°E	Ptolemaeus	3	10°S	3°W
Mare Smythii (Smyth's Sea)	4	3°S	85°E	Pythagoras	1	65°S	65°W
Mare Spumans (Foaming Sea)	2	1°N	65°E	Schickard	3	44°S	54°W
Mare Tranquillitatis (Sea of Tranquility)	2	10°N	35°E	Schiller	3	52°S	39°W
Mare Undarum (Sea of Waves)	2	7°N	68°E	Sinus Aestum (Seething Bay)	1	12°N	8°W
Mare Vaporum (Sea of Vapours)	2	14°N	3°E	Sinus Iridum (Bay of Rainbows)	1	44°N	32°W
Montes Alpes (Alps)	2	45°N	2°E	Sinus Medii (Central Bay)	1,2,3,4	0°	0°
Montes Apenninus (Apennines)	2	22°N	3°E	Sinus Roris (Bay of Dews)	1	52°N	48°W
Montes Carpatus (Carpathian Mountains)	1	15°N	24°W	Stadius	1	11°N	14°W
Montes Caucasus (Caucasus Mountains)	2	34°N	9°E	Taruntius	2	6°N	46°E
Montes Cordillera (Cordillera Mountains)	3	24°S	79°W	Theophilus	4	12°S	26°E
				Tycho	3	43°S	11°W
				Vallis Alpina (Alpine Valley)	1	50°N	3°W
				Vallis Rheita (Rheita Valley)	4	40°S	48°E
				Vallis Schröteri (Schröter's Valley)	1	26°N	51°W
				Vasca da Gama	1	15°N	85°W

Fig. 8 Moon map 1: the northwest quadrant.

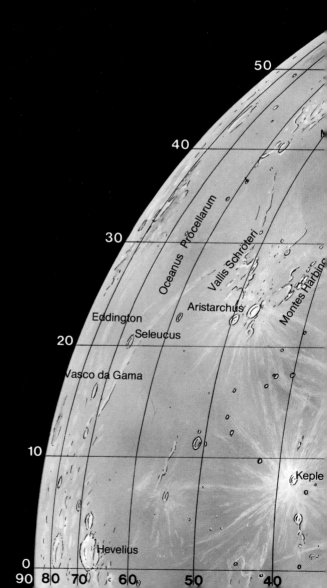

Fig. 8 Moon map 1: the northwest quadrant.

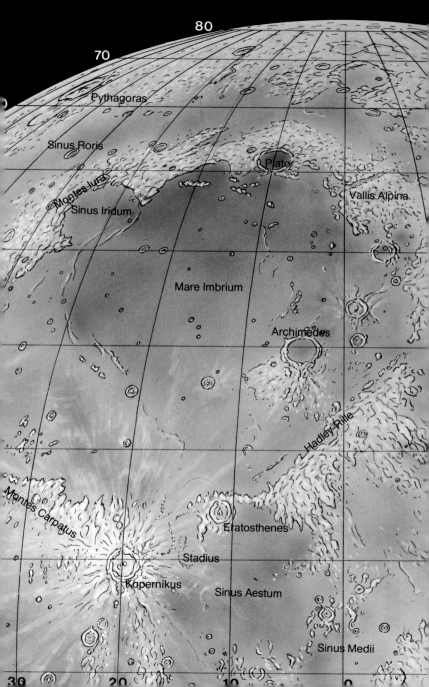

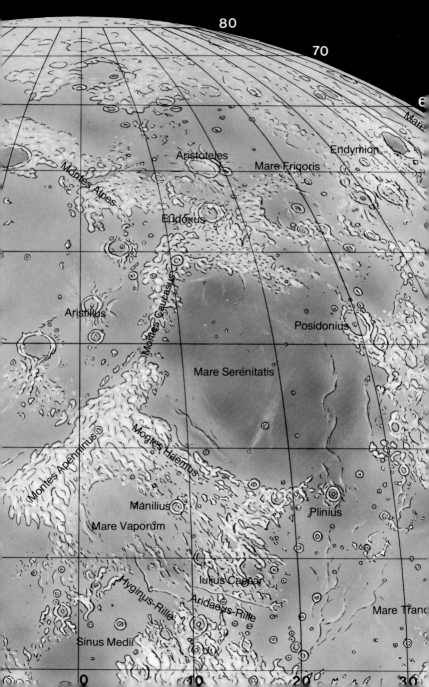

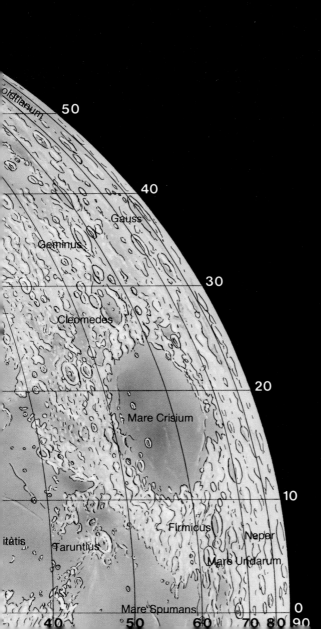

Fig. 9 Moon map 2; the northeast quadrant.

oldianum

50

40

Gauss

Geminus

30

Cleomedes

20

Mare Crisium

10

Firmicus

Neper

itatis

Taruntius

Mare Undarum

Mare Spumans

0

40   50   60   70   80   90

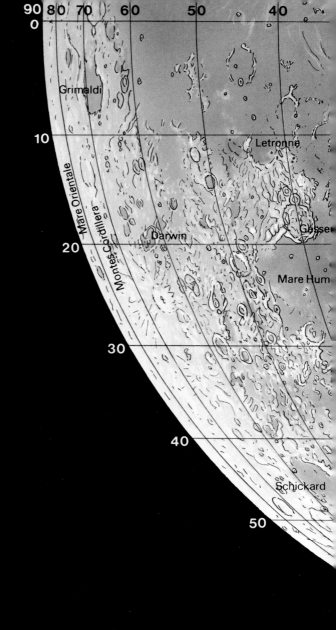

Fig. 10 Moon map 3; the southwest quadrant.

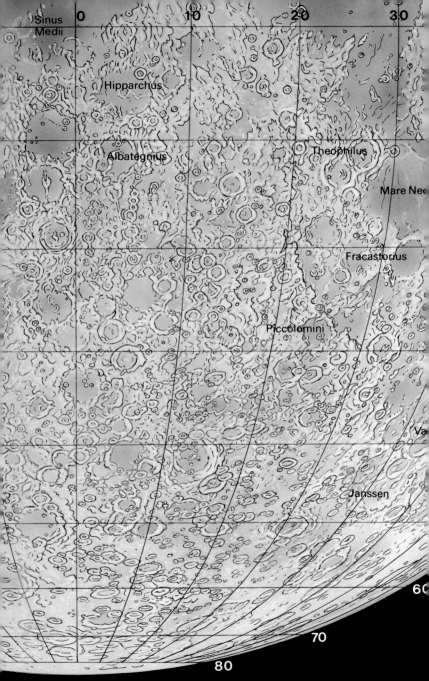

Sinus
Medii

0   10   20   30

Hipparchus

Albategnius

Theophilus

Mare Nec

Fracastorius

Piccolomini

Mare Ne

Va

Janssen

60

70

80

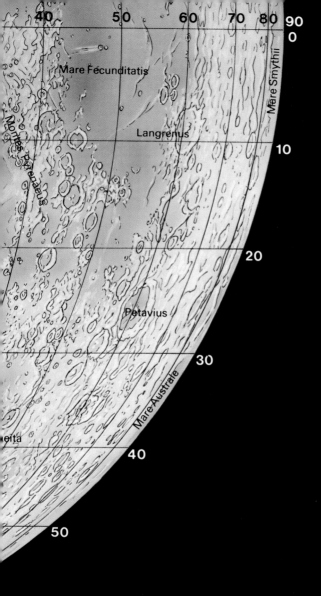

Fig. 11 Moon map 4; the southeast quadrant.

Movements of the planets

The diagrams given on the following pages may be used to gain approximate information about the relative positions of the five major planets until the year 2000. The diagonal bands show the constellations that occur along the ecliptic and are marked with the standard abbreviations. Scorpius and Ophiuchus are treated together, but otherwise the width of the bands represents the length of the ecliptic within each individual constellation.

The position of the Sun is shown by the vertical line running down the centre of each diagram. Planetary elongations east or west of the Sun, measured in degrees along the ecliptic, are shown by the graduations at the top. The order in which the planets rise may be found for any given date by reading from right to left. Planets are in conjunction with the Sun (and thus invisible) when their paths cross the central line. They remain invisible until they pass outside the zone marked by lines 10° on either side of the Sun's position. Objects with western elongations are morning objects, rising before the Sun, and those with eastern elongations are visible after sunset.

For Mercury or Venus, also known as the 'inferior' planets, the planet is between the Earth and the Sun (at inferior conjunction) when the planet is moving westwards in the sky (from left to right). Superior conjunction is indicated by movement in the opposite direction.

An outer planet, Mars, Jupiter or Saturn, is at opposition when its path reaches 180° west of the Sun, at the right-hand edge of the diagram. It then moves into the evening sky (elongations east of the Sun) until conjunction occurs several months later.

The inferior planets show phases similar to those of the Moon, being 'full' at superior conjunction when their angular size is least. As the distance between the Earth and the planet grows smaller (towards inferior conjunction) the planet 'wanes', finally becoming invisible as a much larger, but thin, crescent. The outer planets, also referred to as 'superior planets, on the other hand, show little change in phase from 'full', except for Mars, which is close enough for the unilluminated portion to become noticeable at times.

-------------- Mercury	Jupiter __ __ __ __ __ __
.... Venus	Saturn _____
_ _ _ _ _ _ _ Mars	planetary conjunction o

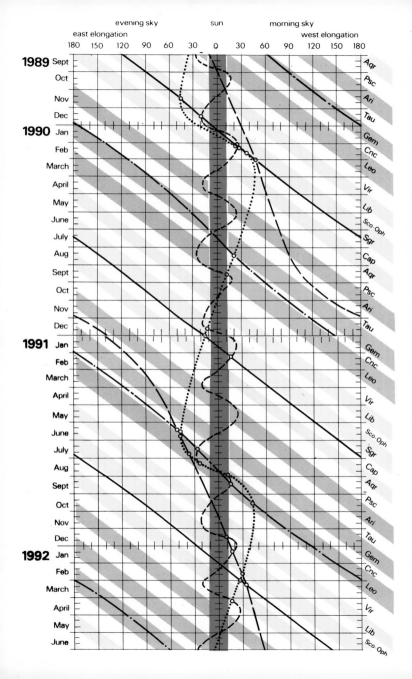

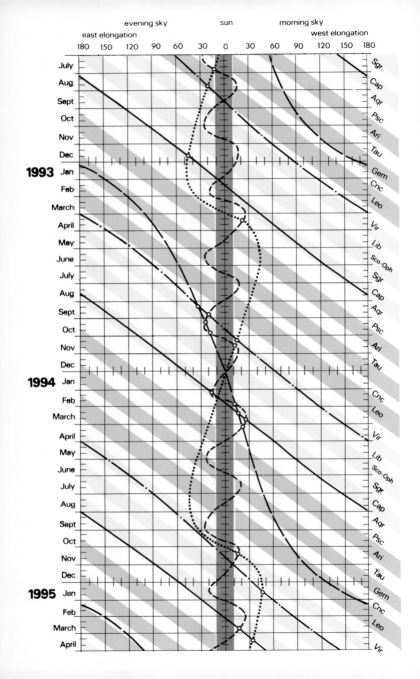

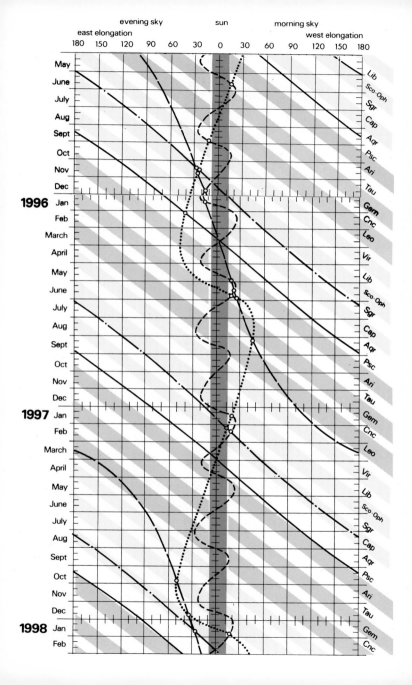

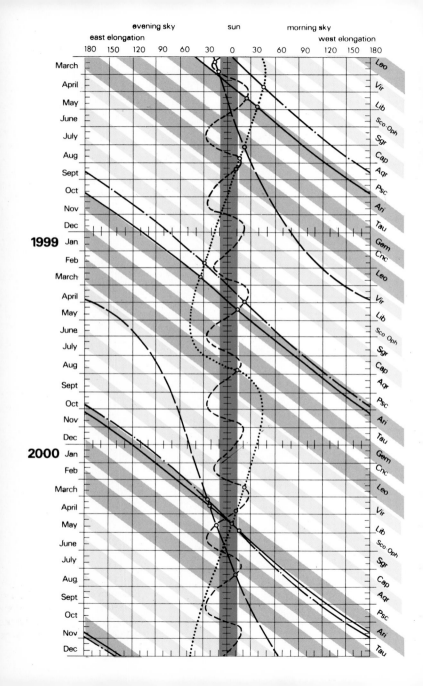

Comet watching

The discovery of new comets has always been one area of observation where amateurs have enjoyed great success. Naturally many comets are discovered by professional astronomers, but this is usually while they are working on some other project rather than due to deliberate searching. However, extreme dedication and an exceptional knowledge of the sky are required, so there are not many observers who undertake comet searches. Most 'comet hunters' tend to use large mounted binoculars or rich-field telescopes (see pages 6–11), and many hundreds of hours of observation are needed before one can remember the star patterns over the whole of the sky and down to the chosen limiting magnitude. Similarly, great dedication is required to search the sky on every possible occasion, especially in those regions of the evening and morning skies near the Sun where comets may creep up and catch us unawares.

Although the orbits of most periodic comets are reasonably well known and predictions usually account for all the planetary perturbations, it is still important that the objects should be monitored at their successive returns. In this way the predictions and orbital elements can be checked and refined. Indeed any information relating to precise cometary positions is of use, and, needless to say, in new comet discoveries such positional measurements are all-important.

Comet photography normally requires the use of wide-aperture optics during the search phase. The field must be sufficiently wide to incorporate fairly bright stars having well-determined positions themselves, hence enabling accurate positional information to be derived for the comet. Similarly, a fast, wide-aperture system is required to ensure that short exposures, minimizing the effects of the comet's motion, still record the comet. In some cases it may be necessary to guide on the comet itself during the exposure. This procedure is used for detailed photographs aimed at recording the structure of the head and tail. As comets are diffuse objects this may pose problems, although sometimes the presence of a star-like nucleus helps to lessen the difficulty. Recording such detailed information in this way is essential if we are to understand the way comets change and evolve with time as they proceed on their journey through the inner solar system. So the more photographs that can be taken of a particular comet, the better. Depending upon the individual object it may be possible to arrange for the drive rates on the right ascension and declination axes to compensate for the cometary motion, but in extreme cases such as fast-moving objects recourse may still have to be made to completely manual methods.

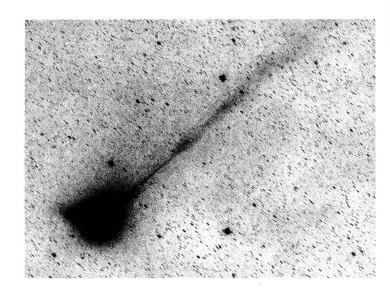

Fig. 12 Comet Wilson on 28 March 1987, three weeks before its closest approach to the Sun (perihelion). It shows the development of a long, weak ion tail, consisting of ionized atoms and molecules which are pushed away from the coma (comet head) by the solar wind. The stars are trailed as the telescope followed the comet during the exposure.

Fig. 13 A 15-minute exposure of Comet IRAS-Araki-Alcock obtained by H. B. Ridley on 10 May 1983, using a 500 mm f/6.3 Ross lens.

Comets are so varied in their brightness, size and features that visual observation may make use of a wide variety of equipment. At times the full extent of long, faint tails may be best perceived by the naked eye, or at most with low-power, wide-field, binoculars. On the other hand, the observation of fine details such as the jets and shells ('hoods') of material being shed by the cometary nucleus may require the assistance of a large telescope, a range of good eyepieces, a keen eye and a skilled observer. Photography cannot record the finest details near the nucleus because of the usually limited resolution, the normal over-exposure in the central regions of the coma, and the short time-scale of the phenomena.

Drawings by experienced observers remain the major source of such information. Unfortunately, too few observers are able to gain much experience of comets because well-placed bright objects are so rare. With previously unknown comets the fact that no-one has any idea of the sort of features or activity which they may show, is one of the reasons – apart from the computation of the orbit – why there is such a flurry of activity amongst observers following the discovery announcement.

Another aspect of cometary studies is that of magnitude estimates. Although these follow the general lines of variable star estimates (see pages 110–114), there are many additional difficulties. One of the problems is that of obtaining accurate magnitudes of comparison stars, as there may not be any suitable ones in the nearby region of sky. The real stumbling-block comes in trying to compare the brightness of an extended object (the comet) with a point source (a star). Various methods involving the defocusing of the images have been devised, but although these are reasonably consistent within themselves, they can never be as accurate as estimates between similar objects, so cometary magnitudes, especially early ones, remain uncertain.

Naturally estimates of a star-like nucleus can be more reliably undertaken, when one is visible. Under many circumstances photographs with ordinary cameras may well be as effective as visual estimates, as happened in the case of the large, close, and very fast-moving Comet IRAS-Araki-Alcock (1983d). Certain normally faint comets, such as Comet Schwassmann-Wachmann 1, can undergo sudden outbursts, so observations are required on every possible occasion.

The general unpredictability of comets means that, as with other 'sudden' events such as novae and supernovae, information must be passed to the observers as rapidly as possible. The official channel through which this happens is the International Astronomical Union's Center for Astronomical Telegrams in Cambridge, Massachusetts, United States, aided by individual countries' alert networks. When a comet is discovered it is usually named after the observer, or observers, who made the discovery. For example, the discovery of Comet IRAS-Araki-Alcock, was reported almost simultaneously, by Araki in Japan, Alcock in England and by the Infrared Astronomical Satellite (IRAS) scientists. It was also given the designation 1983d, meaning the fourth comet discovered in 1983.

Aurorae

The observation of aurora phenomena is quite extensively covered by amateur astronomers and, in its simpler forms, needs very little in the way of equipment. As aurorae occur along the auroral ovals surrounding the north and south magnetic poles, observers tend to be concentrated at fairly high latitudes. However, astronomers at low latitudes should be aware of the fact that they may sometimes be more favourably placed than people at high latitudes. They should take every opportunity to check for the presence of aurorae, and record their form. Auroral activity in the northern hemisphere is referred to as *Aurora Borealis*, while that in the southern hemisphere is the *Aurora Australis*.

The restricted population (and land areas) in the southern hemisphere means that many southern auroral displays are poorly covered, observers on the Antarctic continent being sometimes *too* far south. It is therefore difficult to make correlations between activity seen in the two hemispheres, although this can occasionally be tried.

As was pointed out earlier in the book, the sun goes through periods of intense activity every eleven years. During these times the number of sunspots increases greatly and so does the output of charged particles from the surface. This is a result of highly energetic solar flares. The vast increase in the number of these charged particles impinging in the Earth's upper atmosphere causes the auroral ovals to expand and effectively move to lower latitudes. Reports of auroral displays seen over the mid- to southern parts of the United States are not unusual for a year or so around the time of sunspot maximum. This is much further south than they are usually seen.

Auroral observations are straightforward and involve recording which of the main types are present: arcs (arches with smooth lower borders), bands (irregular lower borders or folds), patches (resembling isolated clouds), veils (widely spread, evenly illuminated areas) and rays (streaks of light extending upwards into the sky). The basic forms may be described as homogeneous, striated (with bands roughly parallel to the lower border) or rayed (appearing to be formed of many individual rays). Further information to record includes details of behaviour (e.g. quiescent or active), brightness, colour and form (e.g. multiple or, if seen at the zenith, coronal). When arcs or bands are seen it is most important to record the elevation above the horizon of the highest point of the lower border. If several observers report this information then the altitude and position of the display can be derived.

Most people are fascinated by the ever-changing forms in an auroral display, and efforts should be made to note full details every hour, and at 15, 30 and 45 minutes past each hour. This procedure should be followed with photography, although naturally one might wish to take additional photographs at intermediate times.

Photography is of great value. Exposures will usually be fairly short, perhaps of the order of half a minute, although this depends upon the speed of the film. Photographs which record the stellar background enable easy determination of the extent and position of a display. There is a lack of knowledge about the precise heights of some of the colours, but photographs taken on modern fast colour films should be capable of being used to determine this.

The magnetic disturbances associated with aurorae can be very marked, and it is possible to construct simple magnetometers which will give an indication of changes in the Earth's magnetic field. Changes in the ionosphere with the occurrence of aurorae affect radio reception, and the detection of such anomalous conditions is yet another aspect which can be followed with comparatively simple equipment.

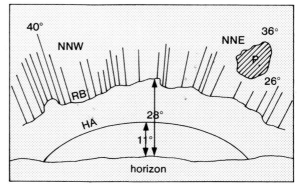

Fig. 14 The positions of auroral features are described by their angular distances from the horizon together with their compass directions. RB = rayed band; HA = homogeneous arc; P = patch.

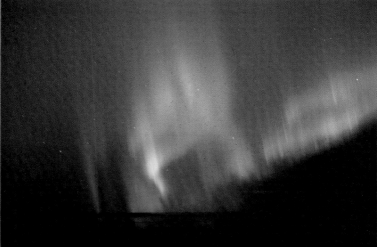

Fig. 15 (*Upper*) An active homogeneous arc (HA), with sharp lower edge and diffuse upper border, photographed from Scotland. The different colours arise from various oxygen emissions. (*Lower*) Active, multiple rayed bands (RB), which were continually altering in shape and strength, illustrate some of the complexity seen in major auroral displays.

The realm of the stars

The celestial sphere

When considering the coordinates of celestial objects, it is necessary to adopt the ancient interpretation of the sky as a sphere
centred on the Earth. We will assume that the Sun moves round the
Earth and that celestial objects move across the surface of the
sphere.

The angle of inclination of the rotational axis of the Earth (or any
other body) does not alter as it orbits its primary (Fig. 16). This
angle, measured from a line perpendicular to the plane of the body's
orbit, is about 23·5° for the Earth.

It is precisely this mechanism that provides the Earth with its
seasons, and points of solstice and equinox are adopted to describe
the effect this has on the spinning planet. Equinox positions mark
the days, in spring and autumn, when day and night are of equal

Fig. 16 As Earth orbits the Sun it moves through positions of equinox, where day
and night are equal in length, and solstice, marking the points at which the Earth's
tilt displays the greatest angle with the plane of the orbit.

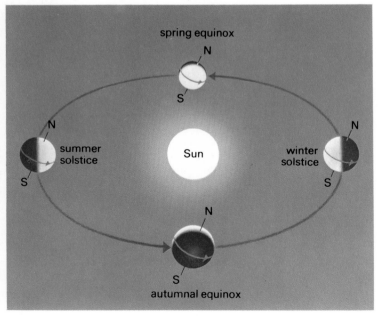

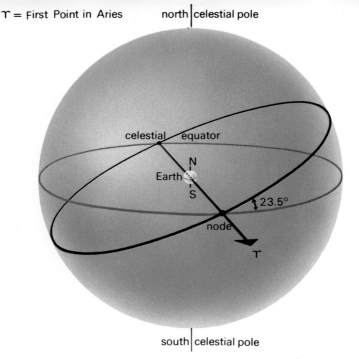

Fig. 17 The Earth's equatorial plane is here projected onto a sphere making it the celestial equator, and the plane of the Sun's path around the Earth is included to become the plane of the ecliptic. The points where the two intersect are called 'nodes' and at present these point to the First Point of Aries.

duration. At such times the Earth's polar axis is at right angles to the Earth–Sun line. Solstice positions, in summer and winter, mark the points at which the Earth's tilt causes the Sun to appear at the greatest distance from the plane of the equator.

In Fig. 17 the Earth's equatorial plane is projected onto a sphere, becoming the celestial equator, and the plane of the Sun's path around the Earth is also drawn on the sphere to become the plane of the ecliptic. The celestial equator has now been given a more usual orientation and the apparent path of the Sun, the ecliptic, is tilted at 23·5°. The points at which the two planes cross, the nodes, establish a geographical coordinate using the line from the centre of the two planes (the Earth) through the spring (vernal) equinox to set up a system of longitude. This point is known as the First Point of Aries.

The north celestial pole is the point on the celestial sphere directly above the Earth's north geographic pole. The lines of celestial

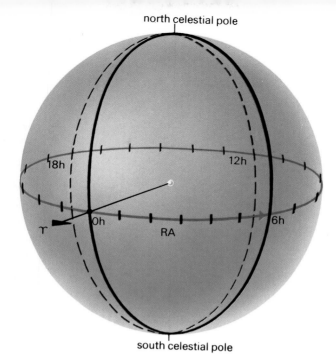

north celestial pole

18h   12h

Ꭳ   0h   6h

RA

south celestial pole

Fig. 18 Lines of celestial longitude are marked in hours, minutes and seconds rotating east around the celestial equator, starting and finishing at the First Point of Aries. This system is known as RA.

longitude are marked eastwards 360° around the equator past the autumnal equinox position and back to the Aries line as in Fig. 18. Unlike the conventional method adopted for the geographic coordinate system, the celestial sphere uses a system of hours, minutes and seconds to mark off longitudes. Moving eastward from the First Point of Aries, or vernal equinox, the 360° circle is divided first into 24 hours of longitude, each divided into 60 minutes and each minute further divided into 60 seconds. This system of celestial longitude is known as Right Ascension (RA).

Having established longitude, it is necessary to construct a system for measuring latitude or elevation from the celestial equator. In Fig. 19, the symbols + and − are used for positions of celestial latitudes north and south of the celestial equator respectively.

To obtain a coordinate for any celestial object, first, the RA is read from the zero meridian. The latitude, or Declination (Dec), is then

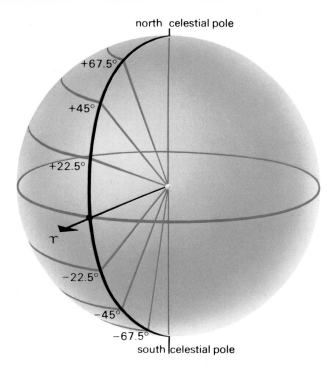

Fig. 19 Lines of celestial latitude from the plane of RA are marked in degrees, + for latitudes north of the plane and − for latitudes south of the plane. Latitude values are referred to as Dec.

found lying between 0° and + or − 90°. This coordinate system is applied to all objects in the universe and although it purports to show celestial phenomena projected onto a sphere, the sophistication of the human mind will accept that the RA and Dec values merely point the eye, or telescope, along a specified line of sight.

Reference to Figs 16 and 17 will show how the Sun moves round the plane of the ecliptic in just over 365 days, and how this causes the day–night cycle to migrate through the constellations. Therefore from a given geographic latitude, observation of the entire visible sky will take one full year. Although it has been necessary to construct a fixed geometrical relationship between the ecliptic and the celestial equator this is only the current situation and the gradual precession of the polar tilt (Fig. 20a) causes a precession of the equinox and a continually changing position for the celestial north pole (Fig. 20b).

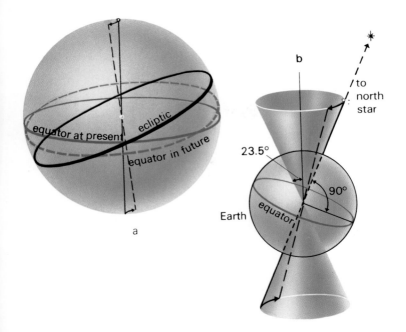

Fig. 20 (a) Precession of the Earth's polar tilt causes a precession of the equinox. This takes place gradually due to the changing relationship of the ecliptic to the celestial equator. (b) Precession of the polar axis also changes the position of the celestial north pole.

The constellations

The following 66 pages of maps and notes are provided so that the reader can develop an understanding of the configuration of the constellations. The first four maps show northern and southern skies for orientation with the celestial sphere.

So that the constellations may be readily recognized, the most significant stars and objects have been included on the charts, some of which therefore show fainter stars than others.

The constellation names are presented in Latin followed by the generic form, the three-letter abbreviation, and lastly the English derivation. The allocation of Greek letters to the stars in each constellation follows the 17th century tradition whereby, in the main, the alphabet proceeds through a sequence of decreasing apparent magnitude (mag). Constellations below 50° south are shown with south at top.

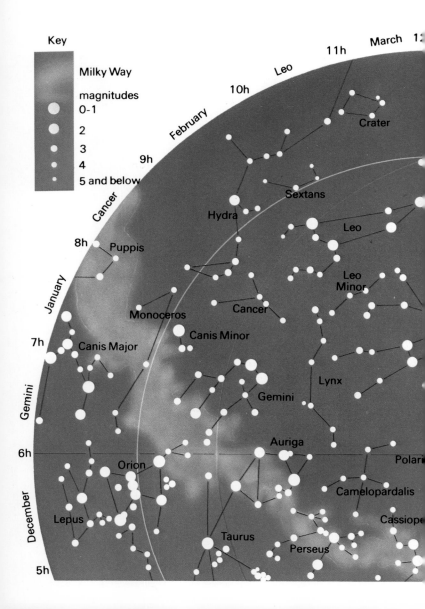

Fig. 21 Northern sky constellations 1.

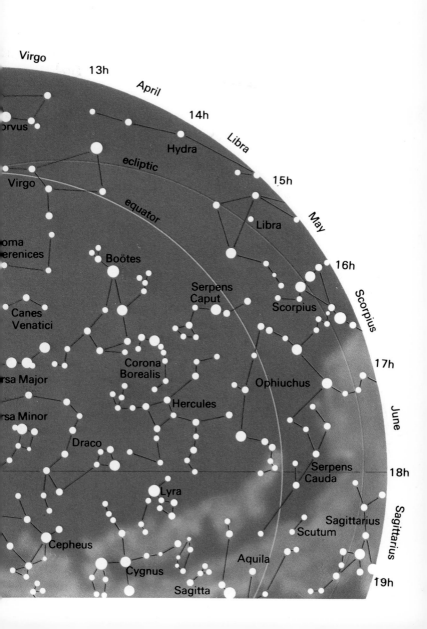

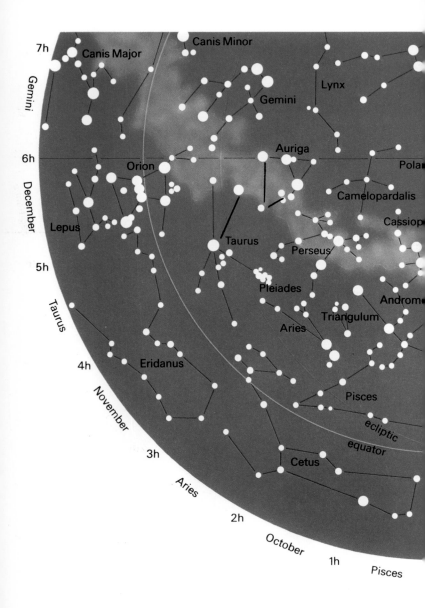

Fig. 22 Northern sky constellations 2.

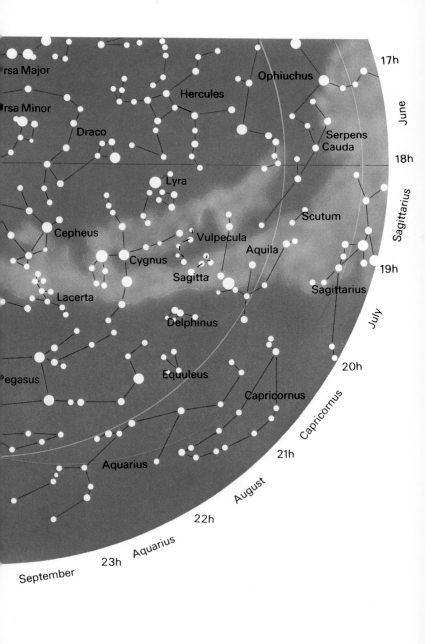

Fig. 23 Southern sky constellations 1.

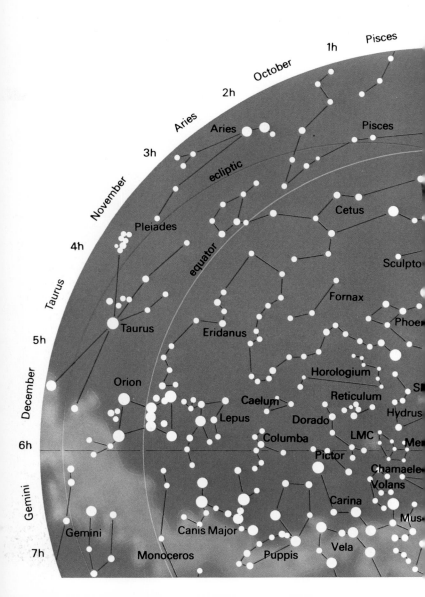

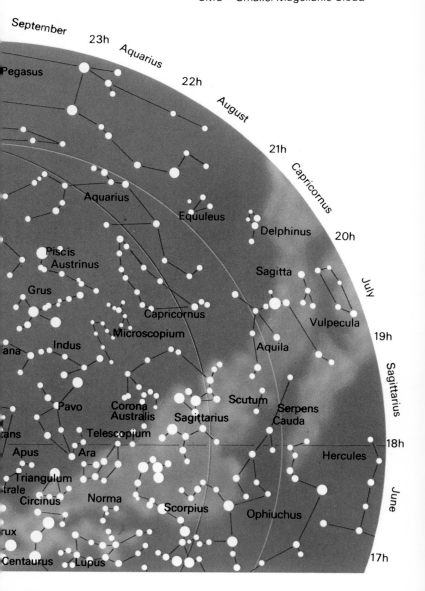

LMC = Larger Magellanic Cloud
SMC = Smaller Magellanic Cloud

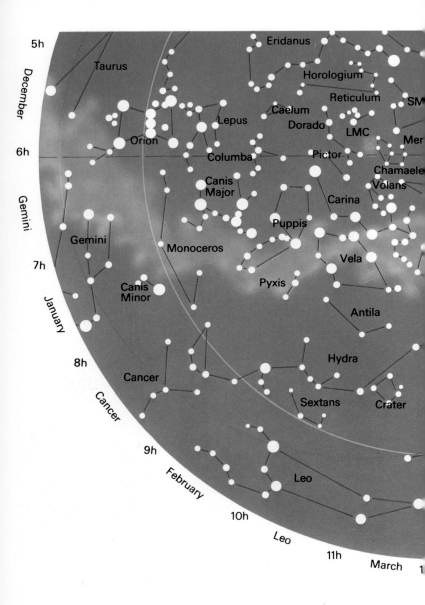

Fig. 24 Southern sky constellations 2.

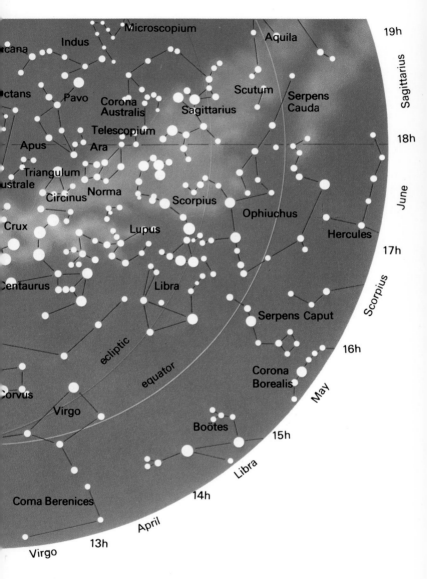

LMC = Larger Magellanic Cloud
SMC = Smaller Magellanic Cloud

Andromeda Andromedae And *Andromeda*
RA: 01 hr, Dec: +35°

This is one of the oldest named constellations and formed part of Ptolemy's catalogue. Mythological legend surrounds the naming of Andromeda and it is one of the best-known groups in the sky, not so much perhaps for the stars it contains, but because it includes M31, a giant spiral galaxy very close to our own. These two are the largest in the Local Group of galaxies which contains about 20 members.

The three most prominent stars are laid out along Dec 30–40 and virtually span the constellation. Star β, Mirach, is a mag 2·02 M0 type with absolute mag 0·2, lying at a distance of 76 light years. Originally in the constellation of Pegasus, and indeed right on the border, can be found α, Alpheratz, a mag 2·06, B9 star with absolute mag +0.1, 90 light years from the Solar System. In the opposite direction towards Perseus, γ, Almaak is a mag 2·14, K3 type with absolute mag −0·1 some 120 light years distant. It is actually a multiple star with components of mag 3·0, 5·0 and 6·2.

Heading almost directly north from star δ, the keen observer will see with the naked eye a faint hazy patch lying on a similar declination to Almaak. This is the Great Andromeda Galaxy, M31, which has a total magnitude of 5·0. The galaxy is about $2·2 \times 10^6$ light years away.

Antlia Antliae Ant *Pump*
RA: 10 hr, Dec: −30°

This southern sky constellation, flanked by Centaurus, Hydra, Pyxis and Vela, is inconspicuous and comparatively unimportant for object content or direction seeking.

Apus Apodis Aps *Bird of Paradise*
RA: 15 hr, Dec: −75°

Apus is another southern sky constellation which was added by Bayer in the 17th century. Originally known as Apus Indica, Apus is flanked by Musca, Chamaeleon, Octans, Pavo, Ara, Triangulum Australe and Circinus. No interesting stars are in this group and the most prominent is the mag 3·8, α.

θ is an irregular variable of spectral class M and varies between mag 5·0 and 6·6.

Andromeda

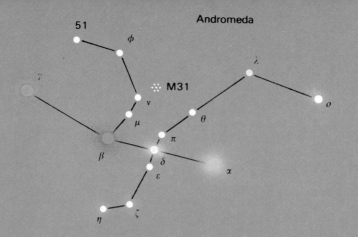

Antila

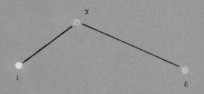

Apus

Magnitudes

1 and over

2

3

4

5

Nebulae and Clusters

Spectral Classes

O – B

A0 – A9

F – G

K – M

Aquarius Aquarii Aqr *Water Bearer*
RA: 22 hr, Dec: −15°
Aquarius is one of the 12 constellations of the zodiac, and one of the oldest named groups. The mythological representation of a water-bearer influenced the Egyptians to believe that its ascendant appearance over the horizon with the Sun brought fertility to the land.

The constellation is flanked by Pegasus, Equuleus, Delphinus, Aquila, Capricornus, Piscis Austrinus, Sculptor, Cetus and Pisces. It extends from RA 20 hr 35 min–23 hr 55 min and from Dec +3 to −25, a sprawling expanse of the ecliptic plane. The brightest star in the group is β, Sadalsuud, of visual mag 2·86, which is very similar to the Sun in class but a supergiant by type. Star α, called Sadalmelik, is of mag 2·96 and from here a triangle of stars can be seen representing the jug carried by the mythological water-bearer. The constellation also contains the Saturn Nebula (named because of its similarity to the ringed planet) and the famous Helix Nebula, NGC 7293.

Aquila Aquilae Aql *Eagle*
RA: 20 hr, Dec: +05°
This prominent summer constellation is named after the mythological eagle sent to carry Ganymede to Olympus. Aquila has consistently been associated with birds and the triangular outline is seen to represent a bird with outstretched wings.

Lying in the general direction of the Milky Way, Aquila is sometimes difficult to pick out from the star clouds beyond. Star α, Altair, is a very bright white star to the east of the apex, only 16 light years from Earth, and is an A7 class star of mag 0·77. It is flanked by γ Aquilae, 340 light years away (mag 2·7) and Alshain (β) (mag 3·9). Star η Aquilae is a prominent Cepheid variable (mag 3·7–4·4) with a period of seven days.

Ara Arae Ara *Altar*
RA: 17 hr, Dec: −55°
Ara has precessed considerably from the position it held when named. It now lies far to the south, but was visible from the Mediterranean in 1000 BC.

Ara is a mediocre collection of stars with members α and β of mag 2·9 and spectral types K3 and B2 respectively. Their respective distances are 390 and 1030 light years from the Sun.

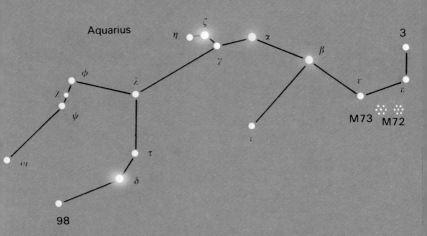

Aquarius

ι φ
ψ
λ
η ζ
γ
χ
β
3
τ
ε
M73   M72
ι
ω
τ
δ
98

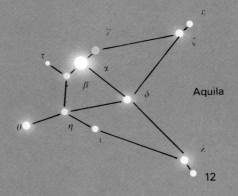

ε
γ
ζ
τ
α
β
δ
Aquila
θ
η
ι
λ
12

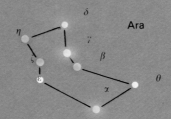

δ
η Ara
ζ γ
β
ω θ
α

Aries Arietis Ari *Ram*
RA: 02 hr, Dec: +20°

Aries, named by the Greeks after the ram with the Golden Fleece, bequeathed its name to the zero point of the system of RA, because the vernal equinox was once located in the constellation. Precession has shifted the equinox into Pisces which, together with Triangulum, Perseus, Taurus and Cetus, borders the constellation.

Aries has only two stars above magnitude 4. These are α, Hamal, with mag 2·0 (76 light years distant) and β, Sheratan, of mag 2·7 (52 light years distant) of spectral types K2 and A5 respectively. The third named star, γ, Mesarthim, is double with mags 4·7 and 4·6. Its name may come from the Arabic word for 'The Sign' and refers to the alignment with the vernal equinox in early history.

Auriga Aurigae Aur *Charioteer*
RA: 05 hr, Dec: +40°

Although it is accepted that Auriga represents a bearded man carrying a goat, the Assyrians viewed this as a chariot and the Greeks saw it as a lame man riding a horse. Auriga achieves fame today from the star ε Aurigae, an eclipsing binary with a 27-year period and a mag 3 component, orbiting the largest star yet observed – an infrared body some $3·0 \times 10^9$ km across, both of which lie 3400 light years from Earth.

The brighter component can be seen through the tenuous envelope of the larger star, and therefore the system appears to be a single variable. ζ Aurigae is an eclipsing binary with a period of 3 years, and the star α, Capella, is interesting since it is a bright (mag 0·05) spectroscopic binary 45 light years away. It has components of 4·3 and 3·3 solar masses and a period of 104 days.

Other prominent stars are β, Menkalina, an A2 type of mag 1·86, ι of K3 type and mag 2·64 and θ a B9 star of mag 2·65.

Boötes Boötis Boo *Herdsman*
RA: 15 hr, Dec: +30°

Boötes is one of the oldest constellations and is mentioned in *The Odyssey*.

The most important star is α, Arcturus, of mag −0·06, an orange K2 type giant lying 40 light years away and 30 times the diameter of the Sun. Arcturus was one of the stars first measured by Halley to have motion relative to the Sun. ε, Izar, of mag 2·4, is a double star often referred to as one of the most beautiful stars in the sky, and frequently given the name Pulcherrima, 'Most Beautiful'.

Other visible elements in the constellation are η, Saak, of mag 2·69, and γ, Seginus, of mag 3·0, 32 and 118 light years away respectively.

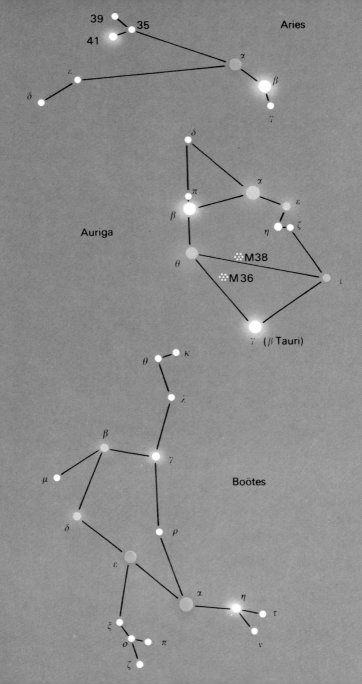

Caelum Caeli Cae *Chisel*
RA: 05 hr, Dec: −40°

This inconspicuous southern constellation is best dedicated to the memory of the little known astronomer Lacaille than to any serious observational activity. Lacaille studied at the Paris Observatory and made major contributions to establishing an accurate measure of the arc of the meridian. Later, from 1751–53, he derived the positions of some 10,000 stars during which time he set up the constellation Caelum. No other astronomer has made a greater contribution to the mapping of southern constellations.

For northern observers Caelum is a winter group and can only be easily seen south of latitude 30°N. It has no objects of any great interest.

Camelopardalis Camelopardalis Cam *Giraffe*
RA: 06 hr, Dec: +70°

This is an inconspicuous constellation occupying a fairly large region of the northern circumpolar sky. Its name, first used by Bartschius in 1614 but believed to have been derived earlier, has been variously given as Camelopardus and Camelopardis.

The constellation occupies a relatively barren region of space and the seven brightest stars are all between mag 4–5. This constellation contains little of interest, although some variable stars are visible with binoculars. Its boundaries are very irregular, especially the eastern one, which meanders towards Ursa Minor with numerous changes of direction.

Cancer Cancri Cnc *Crab*
RA: 09 hr, Dec: +20°

Cancer is an old constellation and one of the 12 zodiacal groups. Several thousand years ago this constellation formed the background to the Sun when the latter reached the summer solstice, its maximum elevation above the celestial equator (23·5°). The Sun was directly overhead along latitude 23·5°N and this line around the Earth was known as the Tropic of Cancer. Precession has now displaced this constellation from the solstice, which currently lies on the border of Gemini and Cancer. Cancer contains 2 stars greater than 4th mag and the only interesting objects are two open clusters, M44 and M67. M44 is displaced from a line joining stars γ and δ centred on Dec +20° and contains more than 300 stars between mags 6 and 12, a group known as Praesepe.

Caelum

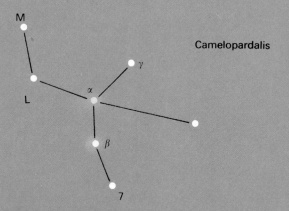

Camelopardalis

Cancer

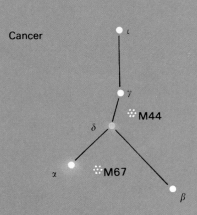

Canes Venatici Canum Venaticorum CVn *Hunting Dogs*
RA: 13 hr, Dec: +40°

Canes Venatici was set up in the late 17th century to fill a gap in Ptolemy's original 48 constellations. It is flanked by Ursa Major, Coma Berenices and Boötes. The only bright star is α, Cor Caroli, a mag 3·2, A0 type, 91 light years from Earth.

The constellation contains four interesting objects other than Cor Caroli. A globular cluster, M3, is located on the extreme southern boundary of the constellation. It contains over 10^5 stars in a sphere 65 light years across, 6×10^4 light years away. M51, close to the north-east boundary, is the famous Whirlpool spiral galaxy. M63, north-east of Cor Caroli, is another spiral galaxy (mag 9·6) as is NGC 4258 (mag 9·2) north-west of star β.

Canis Major Canis Majoris CMa *Big Dog*
RA: 07 hr, Dec: −25°

The most important star in this constellation is α Canis Majoris, Sirius the Dog star, so named because it is the brightest component of Canis Major which, to the Egyptians, represented Anubis, the jackal-headed god. Sirius rose just before the Sun when the Nile was about to begin its yearly flood, and therefore was of great importance in the Egyptian calendar.

Sirius is a mag −1·43 A1 type star less than 9 light years away and is the brightest star in the sky. It is accompanied by a faint companion orbiting $2·9 \times 19^9$ km away in 49·9 years (mag 9·1). Sirius B was the first white dwarf to be discovered. Canis Major contains four other stars brighter than mag 2·5 and also, M41, an open cluster lying 1300 light years away. Many of the stars are in fact intrinsically brighter than Sirius but at very great distances, rendering them visually fainter than this nearby star.

Canis Minor Canis Minoris CMi *Little Dog*
RA: 07 hr, Dec: +05°

Canis Minor is bounded on two sides by Monoceros and contains two stars of interest. Procyon, a mag 0·37, F5 star, 11·5 light years distant, and β, Gomeisa, of mag 2·9 lying 210 light years distant. Procyon is six times solar luminosity, twice the size of the Sun but only 1·1 times the mass. Procyon and Gomeisa are the only two prominent objects in the constellation.

✳ M51

Canes Venatici

✳ M63

Canis Major

Canis Minor

Capricornus Capricorni Cap *Sea Goat*
RA: 21 hr, Dec: −15°

This constellation was associated with the lowest point reached by the Sun below the celestial equator (23·5°) at winter solstice for northern observers. It therefore gave its name to the tropic of Capricorn for latitude 23·5°S.

The main star, δ, Deneb Algedi, is a mag 2·95–2·88 variable A6 type about 50 light years distant. Two naked-eye doubles are of interest. α, Giedi Prima, is of mag 4·2 with a binary companion of mag 9, and Giedi Secunda, is mag 3·6 with a binary companion of mag 11. The second pair, β, Dabih, is very close with mags 3·3 and 6. A globular cluster, M30, lies below Deneb Algedi.

Carina Carinae Car *Keel (of a ship)*
RA: 09 hr, Dec: −60°

Once part of the great sprawling Argo Navis, Carina is now separated (as are Puppis and Vela) and occupies a large portion of the southern sky. The constellation contains the second brightest star in the sky − Canopus, used by planetary spacecraft as a reference point for navigation.

Canopus is mag −0·73, and an F0 type star with an absolute mag of +8·5. Other companions are β, Miaplacidus, a mag 1·67 A0 type 86 light years away, ε Carinae, a mag 1·97, K0 type at a distance of 340 light years and ι, Tureis, a 2·25 mag, F0 star, 750 light years distant. A rich globular cluster, NGC 2808, lies due west of υ, a mag 2·97 A7 star. An interesting variable, η Carinae, grew from mag 4 to rival Sirius in 1843 and then, 10 years later, dimmed to its current mag 6·2.

Cassiopeia Cassiopeiae Cas *Cassiopeia*
RA: 01 hr, Dec: +60°

Two of the main stars in Cassiopeia, α, Schedir, and γ, Tsih, are variable (about mag 2·16 and 1·6–2·9, respectively). The latter has a mag 8·2 companion. Of the remaining three stars making up the famous 'W', β, Chaph, is a mag 2·26, F2 type, δ, Ruchbah, is a mag 2·67 A5 (probably an eclipsing variable with a 759-day period) and ε Cassiopeiae, is mag 3·3.

All but the last are less than 150 light years distant, but ε is 500 light years away with an absolute mag of −2·7. The southern half of the constellation contains part of the Milky Way and many open clusters populate the region including M52 and M103. Cassiopeia lies opposite Ursa Major across the celestial north pole.

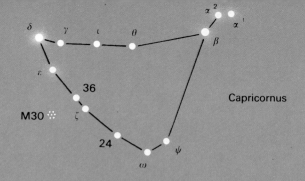

Capricornus

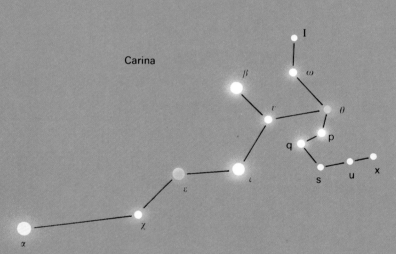

Carina

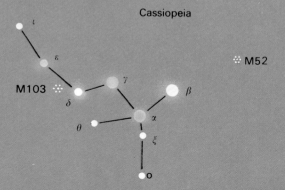

Cassiopeia

Centaurus Centauri Cen *Centaur*
RA: 13 hr, Dec: −50°
Centaurus is a large constellation containing many bright stars, particularly the striking pair α and β Centauri. The α Centauri system is interesting as it is the closest binary to the Sun and has components of magnitude 0·01 and 1·7. A further faint (mag 11) star, known as Proxima Centauri, is believed to orbit the bright pair. It is the closest known star to the solar system and lies at a distance of about 4·3 light years. The other bright star, β Cen, Agena, is 390 light years away and has an absolute magnitude of −5·2.

Containing part of the Milky Way, Centaurus is a fine region to study with binoculars. A bright globular cluster, ω Cen, is easily located by prolonging the line from β to ε Cen. Its actual distance is about 17,000 light years.

Cepheus Cephei Cep *Cepheus*
RA: 21 hr, Dec: +55°
This constellation contains δ Cephei, the prototype Cepheid variable with a mag range of 3·51–4·42 and a period of 5·4 days. α, Alderamin, is an A7, mag 2·44 star, 52 light years away and β, Alphirk, is a variable (mag 3·14–3·19) binary. The only other bright stars of note are γ, Er Rai, a mag 3·2 object, ζ Cephei (mag 3·31) and μ, the 'Garnet Star', which appears a deep red colour.

Cetus Ceti Cet *Whale*
RA: 02 hr, Dec: −05°
The most famous object in Cetus is a striking variable star. Known as Mira, the star o Ceti is a naked-eye object at maximum, even reaching mag 2 on rare occasions. At minimum it is below mag 10 and the variation has a period of about 332 days, taking three months to rise and seven months to decline. The star is an M6 type supergiant about $4·24 \times 10^8$ km across attended by a B-type binary companion in a 400-year orbit. The B star appears to interact with matter ejected from the pulsating supergiant.

Mira radiates 3·5 times as much energy at maximum brightness as it does at minimum. It is the prototype for the long-period (or Mira) variables. Other interesting stars are β, Deneb Kaitos, a K1 type with mag 2·02, and α, Menkar, a type M2 with mag 2·54.

Chamaeleon Chamaeleontis Cha *Chameleon*
RA: 11 hr, Dec: −80°
The constellation is probably best found by locating β and ω Carinae, which lie to the north. The constellation was one of a series named by Bayer very early in the 17th century. The brightest stars in the group are of mag 4, and δ Chamaeleontis is a visual binary.

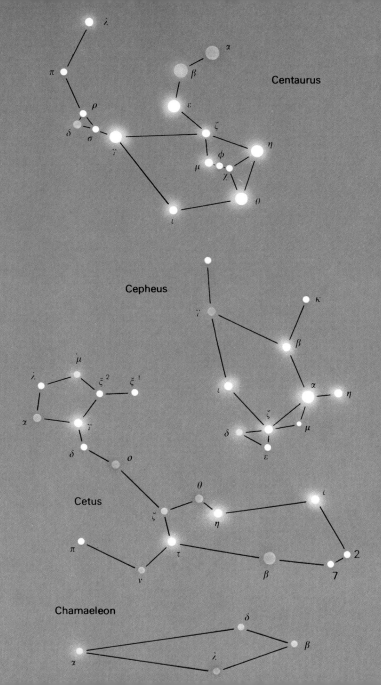

Centaurus

Cepheus

Cetus

Chamaeleon

Circinus Circini Cir *Pair of Compasses*
RA: 16 hr, Dec: −65°
This constellation occupies a small region of the southern sky. It appears to form an elongated triangle and is flanked by Triangulum Australe, Norma, Lupus, Centaurus, Musca and Apus. Had it not been separated by Lacaille in 1763 (when he contributed 14 constellations to the charts) it would more properly be seen as a part of the constellation of Centaurus branching, perhaps, from α Centauri, the closest star system to the Sun. In any event, positive location of the two main stars in Centaurus helps with the identification of Circinus. The only really interesting star in this group is α Circini, a double (mags 3·4 and 8·8) of yellow and reddish appearance respectively.

Columba Columbae Col *Dove*
RA: 06 hr, Dec: −35°
This southern constellation was originally named Columba Noae, which literally translated means the Dove of Noah. The abbreviated expression 'Columba' has now become the official title.

The only two stars of interest are α, Phakt and β, Wezn. Phakt is a B8 type star with an apparent mag of 2·64 and is about 140 light years away. Wezn is of mag 3·2 and lies at the centre of the irregular 'T' formed by the constellation.

Coma Berenices Comae Berenices Com *Berenice's Hair*
RA: 13 hr, Dec: +20°
Added by Tycho Brahe in the 17th century, this constellation is flanked by Ursa Major, Leo, Virgo, Boötes and Canis Venatici. The origin of the name lies in Ptolemaic Egypt when a Pharaoh's sister, Berenice, promised to offer her severed hair to Venus if her husband returned safe from the Syrian wars. He did, but the locks were lost from the temple of Venus and the story was developed that Jupiter had removed them to form the constellation.

There are no stars greater than mag 4·0 in Coma Berenices, but the north galactic pole lies close to a line connecting β and γ and the region is rich in extragalactic nebulae. Since it lies far above the galactic plane there are many external galaxies.

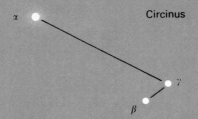

Circinus

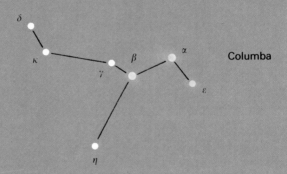

Columba

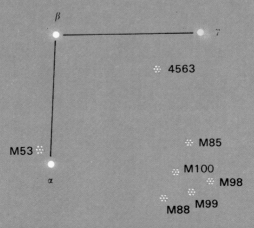

Coma Berenices

Corona Australis Coronae Australis CrA *Southern Crown*
RA: 19 hr, Dec: −40°

One of Ptolemy's original group of 48 constellations drawn up in the second century AD, it lies between Sagittarius and Scorpius. Corona Australis forms an arc apparently lying within the embrace of Sagittarius.

Corona Australis can be found by first locating the stars α, β and ε in Sagittarius. The constellation is then found lying within this triangle. It has been named because of its similarity to Corona Borealis which lies in the northern hemisphere. No prominent objects lie within this constellation and the brightest stars are of mag 4.

Corona Borealis Coronae Borealis CrB *Northern Crown*
RA: 16 hr, Dec: +30°

This group looks very much like a more luminous, northerly duplicate of the Corona Australis, flanked by Boötes in the west.

The brightest star of the group is α, Alphecca, an eclipsing variable with a mean mag of 2·23 and a period of 17·4 days. The A0 type star is 76 light years away and has an absolute mag of 0·4. The star R Coronae Borealis is the prototype of a class of irregular variables. At random intervals it fades from its normal brightness (6·3), dropping by several magnitudes. This is caused by absorption by carbon particles in the stellar atmosphere, and not due to an eclipsing companion.

Corvus Corvi Crv *Crow*
RA: 12 hr, Dec: −20°

Shaped rather like a kite, this southern constellation seems to form the south-western corner of Virgo. The constellation is one of the original 48.

The four brightest stars, β, γ, δ and ε, are all brighter than mag 3·1, although the fifth star in order of apparent mag is α. An alpha designation usually applies to the brightest star in a group. Star γ, Gienah, is a mag 2·59, B8 type at a distance of 450 light years. β is a mag 2·66, G5 type (very similar to the Sun) at 209 light years. Star δ is a double (mags 2·7 and 8·26) with the secondary sometimes called 'The Raven'. ε is a mag 3·04, K3 object at 140 light years distance.

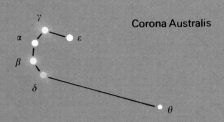

Corona Australis

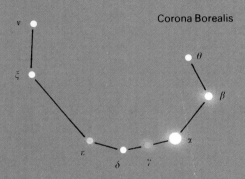

Corona Borealis

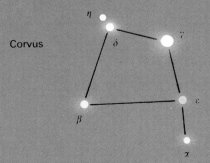

Corvus

Crater Crateris Crt *Cup*
RA: 11 hr, Dec: −15°

This southern sky constellation is flanked by Leo, Virgo, Sextans, Hydra and Corvus. It is very inconspicuous but, nevertheless, one of Ptolemy's original 48 constellations. All the stars are of mag 4 or less.

Crux Crucis Cru *Cross (Southern Cross)*
RA: 12 hr, Dec: −60°

Crux is surrounded on three sides by Centaurus with Musca to the south. The Southern Cross was added to the list of constellations in the 17th century, and is most famous for its almost exact axial alignment with the south celestial pole.

The prime star is α, Acrux, actually a triple system with components of mag 1·6, 2·1 and 4·9. The brighter pair is seen as a single source at mag 0·87 at a distance of 370 light years. Both are B type stars. β, Mimosa, is even further away, at 490 light years, and being a B0 star it has an absolute mag of −4·6. γ is mag 1·68 at a distance of 88 light years and is a M3 star of absolute mag −0·5, δ, Crucis, is a variable star with a mean mag of 2·81 (2·78–2·84) at a distance of 570 light years.

Star ε is of mag 3 and seems ill-placed in this symmetrical system. In the area between α and β and close to the red κ Cru, lies the Coalsack, a famous dark nebula filled with inert dust and gas.

Cygnus Cygni Cyg *Swan*
RA: 21 hr, Dec: +40°

For an obvious reason Cygnus is sometimes referred to as the 'Northern Cross'. α, Deneb, is one of the brightest stars in the sky and with a mag of 1·26 and a distance of 1 600 light years, the star is seen to be an A2 type with an absolute mag of −7·1, 57,500 times the luminosity of the Sun.

One of the most rewarding sights in the sky is the optical double β, Albireo, of mag 3·07, a rich blue K type star 410 light years away accompanied by a golden partner of mag 5. Most of the stars in this constellation are intrinsically bright. An interesting star can be found about halfway between γ Cyg, Sadr, and Albireo. It is χ Cyg, a long-period variable (period 409 days) similar to Mira, o Ceti. It varies between mag 4 and 14. Like most variables of this type, although basically regular, it shows considerable fluctuations in the form of the light-curve.

Crater

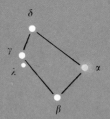

Crux

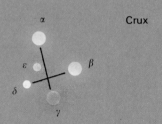

Cygnus

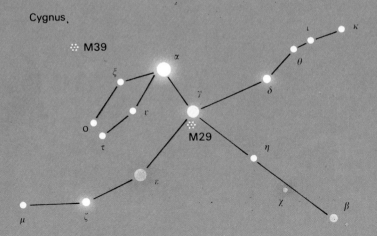

Delphinus Delphini Del *Dolphin*
RA: 21 hr, Dec: +15°

Delphinus lies in a part of the sky that includes several constellations with 'watery' connections (Aquarius, Capricornus, and so
on). It does bear some resemblance to a dolphin, although it has
been likened to a diamond-shaped kite. The two brightest stars are
α, Sualocin and β, Rotanev. These names derive from the reversal of
the name Nicolaus Venator, the Latinized version of Nicolo
Cacciatore, assistant to Piazzi at Palermo Observatory. The star γ is a
well-known telescopic double.

Dorado Doradus Dor *Dorado*
RA: 05 hr, Dec: −60°

This is one of the star groups named by Bayer in 1603. It represents
the fish often incorrectly called a 'dolphin', and it is often (also
incorrectly) said to be a swordfish. There are no particularly
oustanding stars and the only one of note in the group is α Doradus
of mag 3·5. However, the constellation does contain the Large
Magellanic Cloud (LMC) in its southern region. This appears as a
faint patch more than 1 hr of RA in width and centred on Dec −70°.

The Large Magellanic Cloud is so-called because it was first
noted by Europeans during the course of Magellan's expedition
early in the 16th century. Visible to the keen naked eye, the LMC is
an irregular galaxy, the nearest system to the Milky Way galaxy, at a
distance of about $1·7 \times 10^5$ light years. An extremely bright star, S
Doradus varies between mag 8·2 and 9·4. At the distance of the
LMC it has an absolute mag greater than −8.

Draco Draconis Dra *Dragon*
RA: 18 hr, Dec: +60°

Draco is one of the oldest recorded constellations and was known
to the Egyptians, Greeks, Chinese and Arabs under various names.
It spreads in a long chain of fairly isolated stars around a large
portion of the northern circumpolar sky.

The brightest star in Draco is γ, Etamin, a mag 2·21, K5 object
more than 100 light years away. In 3000 BC α, Thuban, a
spectroscopic binary of mag 3·6, was the pole star but subsequent
precession of the equinoxes has now moved Polaris to this position.
β, of mag 2·77, is actually a double star with component mags of 2·7
and 11·5. Draco contains the north pole of the ecliptic lying roughly
between stars δ and ζ on the 18 hr RA arc.

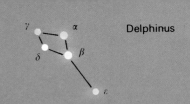

Delphinus

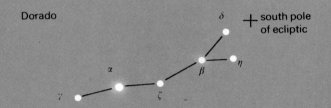

Dorado

+ south pole of ecliptic

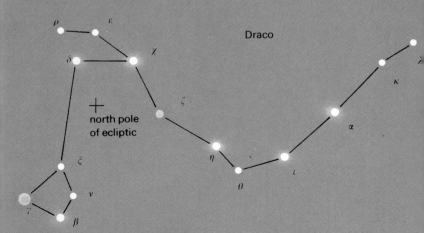

Draco

+ north pole of ecliptic

Equuleus Equulei Equ *Little Horse*
RA: 21 hr, Dec: +10°
Equuleus is a small constellation between Pegasus and Delphinus. Although it is a very inconspicuous group, the constellation is a member of the old list known to the Babylonians. It is best found looking to the west of ε Pegasi, Enif. All the stars in Equuleus are faint, α being just about mag 4, and β is about 1 mag fainter. Nothing of great interest is seen in the constellation but it is well located between Pegasus, Delphinus and Aquarius.

Eridanus Eridani Eri *River Eridanus*
RA: 03 hr, Dec: −25°
Eridanus is supposedly a representation of the celestial equivalent of a river; the Nile to the Egyptians, and the Euphrates to the Babylonians. It snakes an exceedingly sinuous path south of the equator.

The brightest star in the group, α, Achernar, is not visible to observers in the northern latitudes because of the extreme range in celestial latitude covered by the constellation. α has a mag of 0·53 and it lies at a distance of 120 light years with an absolute mag of −2·3. β, Kursa, is a mag 2·8 star of A3 type with an absolute mag of 0·9 and it lies at a distance of 80 light years. θ Eridani, Acamar, was once the end of the constellation, before it was extended to Achernar. The star O_2 is a triple system with the brightest member visible as a yellow dwarf to the naked eye and two extremely faint companions, one of which is a red dwarf and the other a white dwarf.

Fornax Fornacis For *Furnace*
RA: 03 hr, Dec: −30°
This constellation once formed part of the straggling constellation of Eridanus. The name Fornax was given to the constellation by the astronomer Lacaille in the mid-18th century. After naming a nearby group 'The Sculptor', he proceeded to assign this craftsman various tools, including a furnace, with which to accomplish his assumed tasks.

The three stars making up the main configuration take on the appearance of a flattened 'V' and lie in the centre of the rectangular area covered by this constellation. α, mag 3·9, is the only star brighter than mag 4 found in this region.

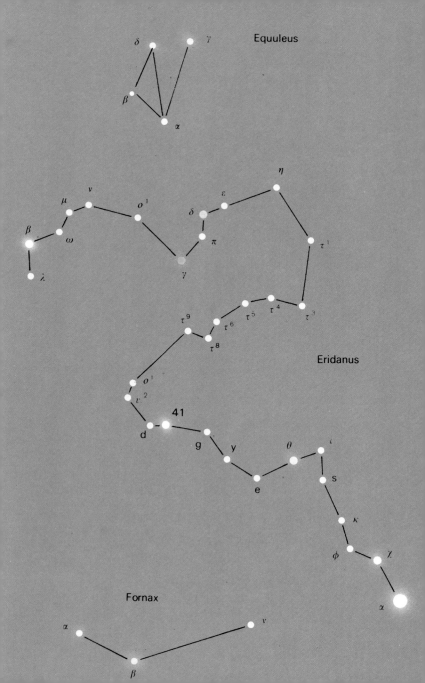

Gemini Geminorum Gem *Twins*
RA: 07 hr, Dec: +25°

Gemini is one of the constellations of the zodiac, where it lies between Taurus and Cancer.

Gemini is most famous for the stars α, Castor, and β, Pollux. Castor, the fainter, appears as a star of mag 1·62. It actually consists of three spectroscopic binaries (mag 1·97, 2·95 and 9·08). All six stars from a single, complex system, which is at a distance of about 45 light years. Pollux is the brightest member of the constellation, a mag 1·16 K0 star, 35 light years distant but intrinsically dimmer than the Castor system.

Alhena is an A type star of mag 1·93 at a distance of 105 light years. μ, Tejat Posterior, is a variable with a mean mag of 2·92 at 160 light years and ε, Mebsuta, is a mag 3, G8 star more than 1000 light years from the Sun. The constellation includes the beautiful open star cluster, M35, best seen with low-power binoculars. Neptune and Pluto were discovered when passing through Gemini.

Grus Gruis Gru *Crane*
RA: 22 hr, Dec: −45°

Grus is a 17th-century constellation probably added by Bayer.

The most prominent stars are α, Alnair, a mag 1·76, B5 star, 65 light years distant, and β, a slightly variable mean mag 2·17, M3 star, nearly 300 light years away. Star γ, Al Dhanab, is a B8 object of mag 3·03 and is in fact the brightest of all three, absolute mag −1·2 but reduced in apparent mag by its 230 light year distance. A 4th mag star, δ, is a naked eye double with two components designated δ¹ and δ².

Hercules Herculis Her *Hercules*
RA: 17 hr, Dec: +30°

This is one of the early constellations, named after the mythical hero.

The central position, 'The Keystone', ε, ζ, π and η is easily found between Corona Borealis and Lyra. The most important star, α, Ras Algethi, is a cool red M type supergiant variable of mean mag 3·5 with a mag 6·1, G type companion. Ras Algethi has been estimated to be up to $4·5 \times 10^{10}$ km in radius which, if true, makes it the largest known star. β, Kornephoros, is a G type 2·8 mag star, 100 light years distant, while ζ and μ Herculis are multiple systems.

An interesting globular cluster, M13, can be found between η and ζ. It is believed to contain more than 10^5 stars in a group 100 light years across. The cluster is about 34,000 light years away, but is just visible to the naked eye.

Gemini

Grus

Hercules

Horologium Horologii Hor *Clock*
RA: 03 hr, Dec: −55°

Horologium was added to the list of constellations by Lacaille in the mid-18th century.

It runs roughly parallel to the end of Eridanus, and can be located from Achernar. In fact its brightest components lie between Eridanus and Caelum.

The most prominent star in Horologium is of mag 3·8 and there is nothing of significance in the rest of the sky occupied by this constellation. It is said to represent an old-fashioned pendulum clock, as used in early observatories.

Hydra Hydrae Hya *Hydra (water monster)*
RA: 10 hr, Dec: −15°

Hydra, the largest of the constellations, snakes a long path between RA 8 hr 10 min and 15 hr. The 'head' of the monster is a small asterism of just six stars with only two greater than mag 4.

α, Alphard, is a red K4 type mag 1·98 object located 94 light years from the Sun and found south-east of the head. ε is one of the two prominent stars in the head and is actually four stars of mags 3·7, 5·2, 6·8 and 12·1. On the borders of Hydra and Centaurus, just below star γ is the galaxy, M83 catalogued as NGC 5236. M68, a globular cluster, can be found between stars γ and ξ. The bright cluster, M48, was 'lost' for many years as Messier had made an error in his original, published catalogue.

Hydrus Hydri Hyi *Sea serpent*
RA: 01 hr, Dec: −70°

This constellation was introduced in the Bayer catalogue of 1603. It is a fairly inconspicuous constellation, largely consisting of a triangle of bright stars, south of Achernar. It also includes part of the Small Magellanic Cloud (SMC) but most of this lies in neighbouring Tucana.

β Hydri is a mag 2·78 star of G1 type at a distance of just over 20 light years. Star α, although not the brightest, is a mag 2·84, F0 type more than 30 light years distant.

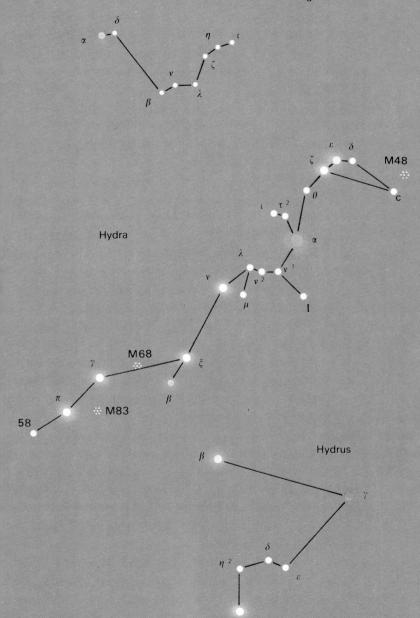

Indus Indi Ind *Indian*
RA: 20 hr, Dec: −50°

Indus is an inconspicuous constellation in the southern sky. It was named by Bayer in his famous atlas, published in 1603. It is fairly easily identified, lying between the stars α Gruis and α Pavonis.

The star α Indi is a mag 3·2 object, the brightest in the constellation. β Indi is close to mag 4, and the other three major stars are all below 4th mag. ε Indi is one of the nearest stars to the Sun, about 11·4 light years distant with a mag of 4·7.

Lacerta Lacertae Lac *Lizard*
RA: 22 hr, Dec: +40°

Named by Hevelius in 1690, Lacerta lies to the south of δ Cephei, the famous variable star. This constellation has few bright members, α, the brightest star, being of mag 3·8.

The most amazing object in this constellation is BL Lacertae. It was originally thought to be a variable star, but it has been shown to be an unusually variable galactic nucleus, much like a quasar. However, its magnitude of 14·7 puts it beyond the reach of all but the larger amateur telescopes. BL Lac lies at a distance of about $8·8 \times 10^8$ light years from the solar system.

No other interesting objects are to be found in this constellation.

Leo Leonis Leo *Lion*
Ra: 10 hr, Dec: +20°

Leo is one of the oldest constellations, and was recognized by many ancient civilizations, including those in Babylonia, Egypt and Greece. It was then close to the position of the Sun at summer solstice.

The most interesting objects in the constellations are α, Regulus, which is double (mags 1·36 and 7·7) of type B7, and lying at a distance of 84 light years. γ, Algieba, is a spectacular double, appearing yellow and green. The combined magnitude is 1·99 and the pair lie at a distance of nearly 200 light years. β, Denebola, is a mag 2·14 A3 type, just 43 light years away.

One of the brightest, intrinsically, in the constellation is ε, Asad Australis, a mag 2·99, G0 type star which is 340 light years away. As would be expected from its close proximity to Coma Berenices and Virgo, Leo contains many external galaxies visible above the galactic plane.

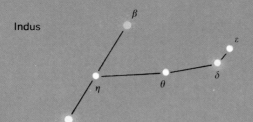

Indus

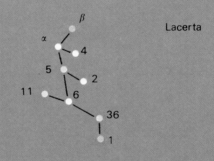

Lacerta

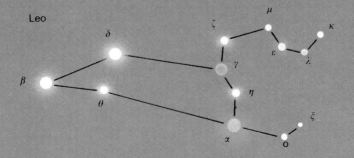

Leo

Leo Minor Leonis Minoris LMi *Little Lion*
RA: 10 hr, Dec: +35°

This constellation was added to the list by Hevelius late in the 17th century and lies between Ursa Major and Leo.

The main star, *o* is a mag 3·8 object similar to the remaining three moderately bright stars of this constellation. Leo Minor is very inconspicuous and contains little of interest to the amateur apart from a few variable stars. A number of faint, distant galaxies are visible in large telescopes.

Lepus Leporis Lep *Hare*
RA: 05 hr, Dec: −20°

Lepus is one of the 48 constellations recognized by Ptolemy. It supposedly represented one of the creatures hunted by Orion, lying, as it does, south of that constellation.

The main star, α, Arneb, is a mag 2·58, F0 type with a distance of 900 light years. Intrinsically less bright, β, Nihal, is a mag 2·81, G2 star (absolute mag −2·1) lying just 320 light years distant. The star is a double with a mag 9·4 companion.

The star ε Leporis is a mag 3·2 object while μ Leporis is of mag 3·3. A 430-day-period variable, R Leporis, is located in the direction of Eridanus and being of mag 6 at its brightest it is just visible to the naked eye but is totally invisible when it dims to mag 10·4.

The globular cluster M79 is found south-west of Nihal; the distance from that star is equal to the distance separating α and β and on a line extended beyond these two stars.

Libra Librae Lib *Scales*
RA: 15 hr, Dec: −15°

Libra is one of the old constellations, and once formed part of Scorpius, to the east. It straddles the ecliptic and is therefore a zodiacal constellation.

The brightest star in the group is the mag 2·61 β, Zuben el Schamali, of B8 type, located 140 light years from the solar system.

Star α, Zuben el Genubi, actually a double, is an A3 type object with an absolute mag of 1·2. Its companion is said by some to be a vivid green even to the naked eye and it has an apparent mag of 5·2. Several noted astronomers, amateur and professional, have refuted this and the coloration seems to depend upon personal eyesight.

Leo Minor

Lepus

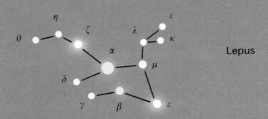

Libra

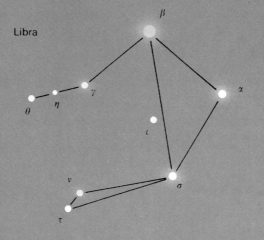

Lupus Lupi Lup *Wolf*
RA: 15 hr, Dec: −40°

Lupus is an original constellation covering most of the region between the bright stars α Centauri and α Scorpii.

The three brightest stars, α, β and γ are all brighter than mag 2·8 and all three exhibit B1 or B2 type spectra. Star α is a mag 2·3 object lying at a distance of 430 light years, and star β is of mag 2·69 at a distance of 540 light years. These have absolute mags of −3·3 and −3·4 respectively, intrinsically very bright sources. Star γ has a visual mag of 2·8, an absolute mag of −1, and is found to lie 260 light years from the Sun. This latter star is a double with individual mags of 3·5 and 3·7.

Star ζ Lupi is another double with mag 3·4 and 3·8 components, and star η is a third double with components exhibiting mags 3·5 and 7·7.

Lynx Lyncis Lyn *Lynx*
RA: 09 hr, Dec: +40°

Towards the end of the 17th century, Hevelius reputedly named this constellation, Lynx, because of the remarkable eyesight demanded of any observer studying this apparently barren area. It lies between 3 important constellations (Auriga, Gemini, Ursa Major) and 3 insignificant ones (Camelopardalis, Cancer, Leo Minor).

Star α Lyncis is a mag 3·2 object 180 light years away. Apart from 38 Lynx (3·9), the remaining stars are less than mag 4 in brightness.

Lyra Lyrae Lyr *Lyre*
RA: 19 hr, Dec: +35°

Lyra was one of the first constellations to be described. Star α, Vega, second brightest in the northern hemisphere, is a class A0 object of mag 0·04 at a distance of 26 light years (absolute mag 0·5) with a mag 10 companion.

Star β, Sheliak, is an eclipsing variable (mags 3·4–4·1) with a mag 7·8 companion. Star ε is actually two stars, one of mag 5·0 with a mag 6·1 companion and one of mag 5·2 with a mag 5·5 companion. Each pair is a binary and the entire group is bound gravitationally.

Yet another double, ζ Lyrae, is found midway between δ and α with components of mag 4·3 and 5·9. Lyra incorporates a nova, reported in 1919, due south of the midpoint between stars β and γ and a globular cluster, M56, south-east of star γ and in almost a direct line drawn from star α through γ.

The famous Ring Nebula, catalogued as M57 (NGC 6720) is located almost half way along a line drawn from γ to β. This is a classic planetary nebula and was caused by the central star of mag 15 shedding a shell of material.

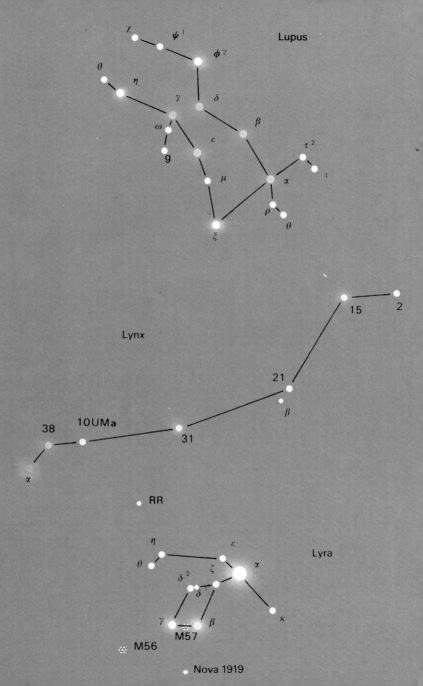

Mensa Mensae Men *Table (Mountain)*
RA: 06 hr, Dec: −75°

This constellation was originally named Mons Mensae by Lacaille, whose observatory was at Cape Town in South Africa.

The constellation contains about 20 stars of mag 5 but none of these is particularly interesting. The most notable claim to fame for this constellation comes from its partial occupation by a section of the LMC, itself more properly sited in Dorado. The faint star β is located in the centre of the Tarantula nebula, the most conspicuous feature of the Large Magellanic Cloud.

Microscopium Microscopii Mic *Microscope*
RA: 21 hr, Dec: −35°

Microscopium is one of the few constellations that are rectangular and have straight boundaries. Once again, it is an insignificant area named by Lacaille. There is little of observational interest in the entire constellation.

Monoceros Monocerotis Mon *Unicorn*
RA: 07 hr, Dec: 00°

The constellation was named by Hevelius in his atlas published in 1690. It lies across the celestial equator, and is also crossed by the main band of the Milky Way.

None of the main stars in the constellation are very bright, α, γ and δ all being approximately magnitude 4·1. M50 is an open cluster, best observed with a small telescope. NGC 2264 is visible to the naked eye and lies close to the irregular variable S Mon. The famous and beautiful Rosette Nebula is NGC 2237–9.

Mensa

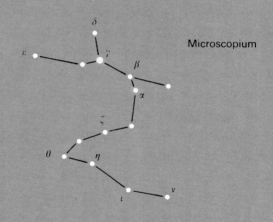

Microscopium

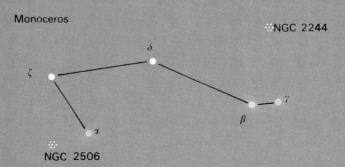

Monoceros

NGC 2244

NGC 2506

Musca Muscae Mus *Fly*
RA: 13 hr, Dec: −70°
This constellation, sometimes known as Musca Australis (Southern Fly), is one of those entered in the 1603 Bayer catalogue. It lies to the south of α Crucis and the famous 'Coalsack' dark nebula.

The star α Muscae is a mag 2·7 variable (mag 2·66–2·73) of B3 spectral type situated 430 light years from the solar system. Star β Muscae, mag 3·06, is a B3 double with component mags of 3·7 and 4·1 and the system lies at a distance of about 470 light years.

Norma Normae Nor *Level (square)*
RA: 16 hr, Dec: −55°
This southern constellation was originally called Norma et Regula (the 'square and level') and was intended by Lacaille to represent some of the tools used by Sculptor.

There are no particularly interesting stars in Norma and all are dimmer than mag 4. An interesting open cluster, NGC 6067, is located on a line from ε through γ and lies close to the star χ.

Octans Octantis Oct *Octant*
RA: 22 hr, Dec: −85°
Octans is the constellation that contains the southern celestial pole. It was named by Lacaille, being originally 'Hadley's Octant' from the important navigational instrument, later replaced by the sextant (also represented in the sky).

The brightest star, υ, is mag 3·7 and the closest star to the actual pole is δ, a dim object of nearly mag 6·0. Apart from the important relationship with the celestial sphere, the constellation contains little of observational interest.

Ophiuchus Ophiuchi Oph *Ophiuchus (serpent bearer)*
RA: 17 hr, Dec: 00°
When the zodiac was originally named, the ecliptic did not cross Ophiuchus, so the constellation was not included. Due to precession, the Sun now spends quite a long period in the constellation, which also lies across the celestial equator.

The most prominent star in the constellation is Ras Alhague, north of the celestial equator and just south of Hercules. The star is a mag 2·09, A5 type located 58 light years from the solar system with an absolute mag of 0·8. Star η, Sabik, is a mag 2·46 object, actually a double with components of mag 3·0 and 3·4, with an A3 spectrum and an absolute mag of 1·4 at a distance of 70 light years.

Star ζ, Han, found almost due north-east from Sabik, is a mag 2·57, O9 type star with an absolute mag of −4·3. It lies at a distance of more than 500 light years. At the other end of the spectral scale

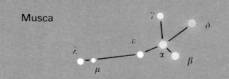

Musca

Norma

※ NGC 6067

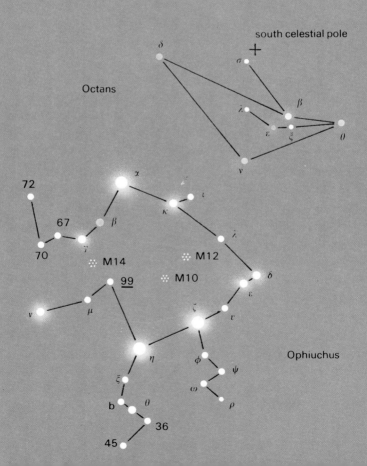

south celestial pole

Octans

Ophiuchus

※ M14

※ M12

※ M10

99

the observer can find δ, Yed Prior, on the boundary with the constellation Serpens Caput. This is an M1 type star with mag 2·72, absolute mag −0·5, and a distance of 140 light years.

Star β, Cheleb, another interesting object, is a K2 type, mag 2·77 object (absolute mag −0·1) at a distance of 124 light years. Three faint globular clusters can be seen located within the area of a triangle set up by straight lines joining Yed Prior and stars γ and μ. These clusters, M10, M12 and M14, are all extremely remote. Globular cluster M9 is adjacent to a line joining stars η and ζ. M19 is south-west of θ.

Orion Orionis Ori *Orion*
RA: 05 hr, Dec: 00°
This prominent and interesting constellation lies across the celestial equator, so it is well-known to all astronomers. The three most interesting stars in this group form the famous belt of Orion: ζ, Alnitak, ε, Alnilam, and δ, Mintaka. Alnitak is a remote double with component mags of 1·9 and 4·05 (system mag of 1·79); Alnilam is a supergiant star of type B0 at a distance of 1600 light years (as is Alnitak) with an absolute mag of −6·8; and Mintaka is an eclipsing variable (mag 2·2–2·35) with a mag 6·47 companion and a period slightly less than six days.

The upper part of the constellation is marked by α, Betelgeuse, (mag 0·5–1·1 variable, M2 type) and γ, Bellatrix (mag 1·64, B2 type). To the south lie χ, Saiph (mag 2·06, B0 type), and β, Rigel (mag 0·08, B8 type of absolute mag −7·1, distance 900 light years). A striking quadruple system is that of σ Orionis, southwest of Alnitak. Slightly farther south lies the Great Orion Nebula, faintly visible to the naked eye, and a magnificent sight in any telescope. The vast cloud of gas is largely illuminated by the stars of the Trapezium, θ Orionis, all young stars between 6th and 8th magnitude.

Pavo Pavonis Pav *Peacock*
RA: 20 hr, Dec: −60°
This constellation is one of those named by Bayer in 1603. The brightest star is α Pavonis, on the very border of Indus and Telescopium. It is a mag 1·95, B3 star (abolute mag −2·9) and is 310 light years away. χ is a mag 4·0–5·5 Cepheid variable with a period of just over nine days. There is one interesting globular cluster, NGC 6752.

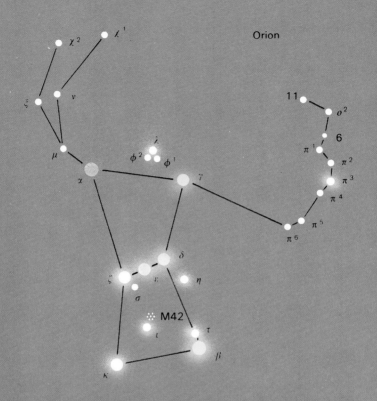

Orion

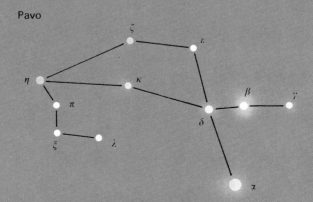

Pavo

Pegasus Pegasi Peg *Pegasus (winged horse)*
RA: 22 hr, Dec: +20°
Pegasus can be recognized by the prominent square formed by three member stars (β, α and γ) and α, Alpheratz, in the neighbouring constellation of Andromeda. Alpheratz lies on the very border of the two designated areas.

The three corners of the square of Pegasus are all above mag 3 and are good observational objects. Star β, Scheat, is a large M2 variable red giant (absolute mag −1·5) at a distance of 210 light years and may range between 2·4 and 2·7. Star α, Markab, is a white B9 of mag 2·5 and γ is a mag 2·84, B2 type (absolute mag −3·4) at distances of 110 and 570 light years respectively. Northwest of β lies η, Matar, a mag 2·95, G8 star.

Star ε, Enif, is a mag 2·4, K2 type star with a mag 11·2 companion. Enif is nearly 520 light years away and has an absolute mag of −4·6. Northwest of ε lies M15, a 6th magnitude globular cluster.

Perseus Persei Per *Perseus*
RA: 03 hr, Dec: +40°
Perseus, one of the earliest named constellations, lies between Cassiopeia and Auriga in the northern Milky Way.

The most interesting object in Perseus is β, Algol, an eclipsing binary and a prototype of this class of variable star. Algol, a mag 2·06–3·28, B8 type star, lies at a distance of 105 light years and is accompanied by a companion of similar size just $1·6 \times 10^7$ km away. The period of the components is just under three days but a third, much smaller, star orbits the binary system in 23 months.

The brightest star in Perseus is α, Mirfak, a giant F5 of mag 1·8 surrounded by several much fainter stars. ζ Persei is a double with mag 3 and 9 components; ε is another double with mags 3 and 8 and ρ Persei is a mag 3·2–3·8 variable. The open clusters h and χ are magnificent objects in low-power instruments. M34 is a very loose open cluster, while M76, near φ, is a faint planetary nebula.

Phoenix Phoenicis Phe *Phoenix*
RA: 01 hr, Dec: −45°
This Bayer constellation is named after the mythological bird that rose from the ashes following repeated burning.

Phoenix is not very conspicuous and contains only six stars above mag 4. The brightest star in this assemblage is α, Ankaa, a mag 2·39, K0 type lying at a distance of 93 light years. Star β Phoenicis is a double with prime and secondary object mags of 4·1 each. Star γ is a mag 13·4 object as is star ζ with a mag 8·4 companion. The constellation is best found by locating Achernar, a mag 0·53 star in Eridanus.

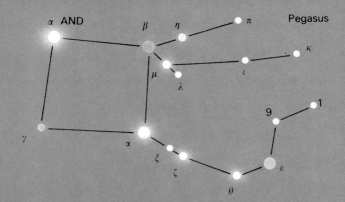

Pegasus

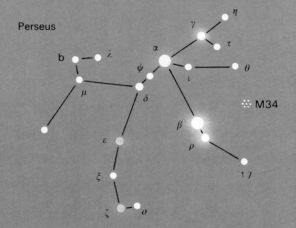

Perseus

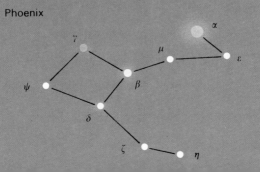

Phoenix

Pictor Pictoris Pic *Easel*
RA: 06 hr, Dec: −60°
The constellation is found by locating the mag −0·73 star Canopus in the constellation Carina.

The only bright stars of note are α and β. Star α Pictoris is a mag 3·27 object and star β Pictoris is of mag 3·9. A nova which flared up in 1925, RR Pictoris, can be found adjacent to star α. It is still visible but a large telescope is required to see anything significant.

Pisces Piscium Psc *Fishes*
RA: 00 hr, Dec: +10°
Although it is unspectacular, Pisces has been recognized as a zodiacal constellation since the days of the earliest civilizations. It lies on the southern and eastern sides of the great square of Pegasus. Due to precession, the vernal equinox, once in Aries, is now well into Pisces.

The most prominent object in Pisces is η Piscium (mag 3·6) followed by α, Alrisha, of mag 3·79, actually a double with mag 4·32 and 5·1 components. A galaxy recorded by Charles Messier, M74 in the catalogue, is found adjacent to star η.

Piscis Austrinus Piscis Austrini PsA *Southern Fish*
RA: 23 hr, Dec: −30°
Piscis Austrinus, one of the originally named constellations, lies between Aquarius and Grus. The only really interesting object in the entire constellation is the magnificent white star Fomalhaut, an A3 type of mag 1·19 and absolute mag 2·0, lying at the comparatively close distance of 23 light years. It is 11 times as luminous as the Sun. All the remaining members of this constellation are below mag 4.

Pictor

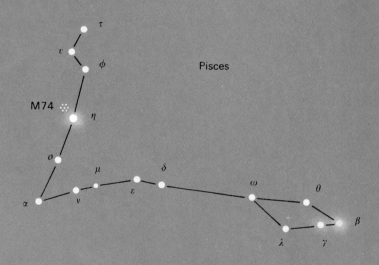

Pisces

M74

Piscis Austrinus

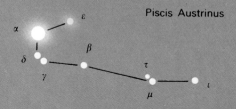

Puppis Puppis Pup *Stern (of a ship)*
RA: 07 hr, Dec: −35°
Puppis was one of the three constellations that originally formed
the sprawling and unwieldy Argo Navis – one of the 48 Ptolemaic
constellations and now separated into Puppis, Carina and Vela.
Puppis can be found best, like Pictor, by first locating Canopus (in
the constellation of Carina) and seeking the pattern of stars which
lies north of this.

The brightest star in the group is ζ, Suhail Hadar, with a mag of
2·23 at the tremendous distance (comparatively) of 2400 light
years giving it an absolute mag of − 7·1. It is a very hot, and rare type
of star with an O5 spectrum.

The only other moderately interesting star is τ, a mag 2·97, K0
type with absolute mag 0·1 at a distance of 125 light years. There
are several open clusters in the constellation, the brightest, M47,
being visible to the naked eye. M46 and M93 are fainter, but still
striking objects to observe.

Pyxis Pyxidis Pyx *Compass*
RA: 09 hr, Dec: −35°
Probably *the* most inconspicuous of all the constellations, Pyxis
was named by Lacaille and appears insignificant beside the original
Argo Navis constellation, now divided into Carina, Puppis and
Vela. Pyxis is surrounded by Hydra, Puppis, Vela and Antlia. It
contains no stars of note.

Reticulum Reticuli Ret *Net*
RA: 04 hr, Dec: −65°
Although usually included as one of the Lacaille constellations,
Reticulum was defined earlier by a German called Habrecht. Rather
than a net it actually represents a reticle, the grid of lines in the
eyepiece of a telescope, used for defining stellar positions. It is
easily located, northwest of the LMC. Only α Reticuli of mag 3·3,
actually a double with components mags of 3·33 and 12 is of
interest.

Puppis

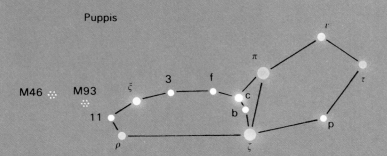

M46   M93

ξ   3   f
11   c
ρ   b
         ζ   p
      π   τ
         r

Pyxis

γ   α   β

Reticulum

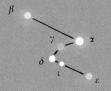

β
γ   α
δ
ι   ε

Sagitta Sagittae Sge *Arrow*
RA: 20 hr, Dec: +18°
Sagitta was one of the Ptolemaic constellations, and lies across the Milky Way, north of Altair in Aquila. Sagitta contains only faint, uninteresting stars but it can be seen to possess a globular cluster, M71, approximately between stars γ and δ.

Sagittarius Sagittarii Sgr *Archer*
RA: 18 hr, Dec: −30°
Of the 88 constellations, Sagittarius probably contains the most abundant and wide-ranging collection of objects. Within its area lie stars, the galactic nucleus, gaseous nebulae, open and galactic clusters – the list is virtually all embracing. It straddles the ecliptic and thus forms one of the zodiacal constellations.

The stars in Sagittarius receive Greek designations totally out of order with their measured apparent magnitude. The brightest star is ε, Kaus Australis, a mag 1·81, B9 type at 124 light years. Next is σ, Nunki, mag 2·12, a B2 star at 300 light years, followed by ζ, Ascella, a mag 2·61 of A2 spectrum, which is actually a double with mags 3·3 and 3·5. δ, Kaus Meridionalis, is less bright again of mag 2·71 with K2 spectrum and an absolute mag of 0·7, at a distance of 85 light years.

Star λ, Kaus Borealis is another K2, mag 2·8, at 71 light years distance, followed by γ, Al Nasl, of mag 2·97, a K0 type at 124 light years. Star η is actually a double with component mags of 3·17 and 10. A triple system, seen as star π Sagittarii, has mags of 3·7, 3·8 and 6·0. Elsewhere, the constellation displays the Trifid Nebula, M20, a faint and complex gas cloud, the Lagoon Nebula, M8, and the Horse-shoe Nebula, M17. Globular clusters M22, M28, M69, M70, M54, M55 and M75 are to be found as well as open clusters M18, M24, M25, M23 and M21.

Scorpius Scorpii Sco *Scorpion*
RA: 17 hr, Dec: −35°
This is one of the zodiacal constellations, although the Sun only takes about a week to pass across it. The most interesting object by far is α, Antares, a supergiant variable (mag 0·86–1·02) with a distinctly green mag 6·5 companion. Antares has a diameter of about 563 million km with an M1 spectra and lies at a distance of 520 light years.

Star ε is a mag 2·28, K2 type at some 66 light years distance and stars δ, Dschubba, β, Graffias, τ, σ, π and μ are all B types within a range of mag 2·34–2·99, situated between 520 and 750 light years in distance. Other objects of interest in Scorpius include two globular clusters, M4 and M80, both of which are to be found fairly

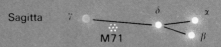

Sagitta

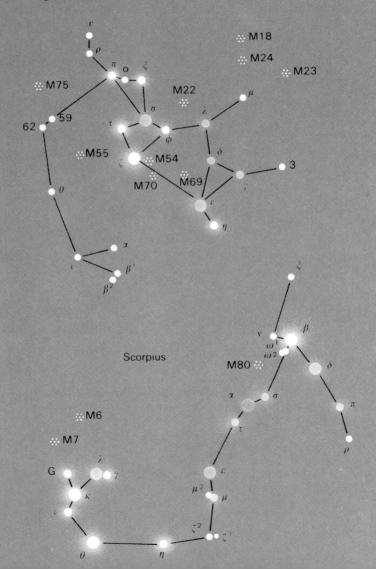

close to Antares. An open cluster, M6, is located within Scorpius as is M7, a much larger open cluster and one which is nearly lost in the great stellar clouds of the Milky Way.

Sculptor Sculptoris Scl *Sculptor*
RA: 01 hr, Dec: −30°
Sculptor lies to the east of Fomalhaut, α Piscis Austrini, from which it is best located. Sculptor contains the south galactic pole and few interesting stars. The most accurate position of the south galactic pole is on a point slightly north of a line drawn from star α to star ι. Little of note is contained in this constellation, although NGC 253 is a fairly bright galaxy.

Scutum Scuti Sct *Shield*
RA: 19 hr, Dec: −10°
Named by Hevelius in 1690, Scutum is an inconspicuous patch of sky to the naked eye but a glorious crowded portion of the Milky Way through even a small telescope.

There are several stellar clusters, the most notable being M11 and M26. M11, the Wild Duck cluster, presents a very striking appearance. It probably contains over 600 stars in a region some 21 light years across, while its distance is about 6000 light years. R Scuti, just to the northwest, is an interesting binocular variable. δ Scuti is the prototype of a class of pulsating variable stars.

Serpens Serpentis Ser *Serpent*
Serpens caput (serpent's head)
Serpens cauda (serpent's tail)
RA: 16 hr, Dec: +05°
This constellation is divided into two: Serpens Caput and Serpens Cauda. It signifies the snake with which Ophiuchus is struggling and this certainly seems appropriate, for the two halves are separated by that constellation.

The only prominent star here is α, Unuk al Hay, a mag 2·65 object. The remainder in Serpens Caput are faint but one of the brightest globular clusters, M5, is in this region. The brightest star in the other half of the constellation is η mag 3·4. M16 combines a star cluster and nebulosity, while I 4756 is a very scattered open cluster.

Sextans Sextantis Sex *Sextant*
RA: 10 hr, Dec: 00°
This constellation forms almost a perfect square and it is flanked by Leo, Hydra and Crater. The constellation was officially named by Hevelius in the late 17th century, but is uninteresting, containing only a few very faint doubles, variables and other objects.

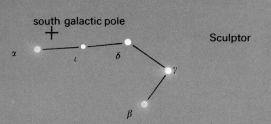

south galactic pole

Sculptor

α ι δ

γ

β

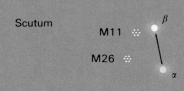

Scutum

M11

M26

β

α

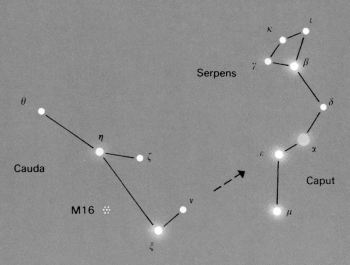

κ ι

γ β

Serpens

δ

θ

η ζ

ε α

Cauda

Caput

M16

ν

ξ

μ

α

β

Sextans

δ

γ

Taurus Tauri Tau *Bull*
RA: 05 hr, Dec: +20°

Taurus, the Bull, was probably one of the first constellations to be named, and is reminiscent of the oldest domesticated animal. Prior to 3000 BC, Taurus lay across the vernal equinox. It is a remarkably rich area of the sky, containing some very prominent stars, the Pleiades and Hyades clusters, and the faint but very important Crab Nebula.

The most magnificent star, α, Aldebaran, is a K5 type giant with mag 0·86, and absolute mag −0·7, at a distance of 68 light years. It is a variable star with a diameter of about 50 million km and a luminosity 120 times that of the Sun. Star β, El Nath, is a mag 1·65 B7 type (absolute mag −3·2) at a distance of 300 light years.

Star η, Alcyone, is another B type with a mag of 2·86, as is star ζ with a mag of 3·07. These latter stars are 540 and 490 light years distant respectively. The Pleiades are found around Alcyone for that star is the most prominent member of this group, which actually consists of about 300 stars. When viewed through the telescope, many very young, hot blue stars can be seen. Under favourable conditions some slight indications of the nebulosity, covering most of the area, may be visible. The system, with all parts moving through space together, is about 500 light years away.

Closer to Aldebaran the observer will find the Hyades, a cluster of nearer stars almost 130 light years away. Not far from ζ is the Crab Nebula, the remnant of a supernova that was seen to erupt in 1054 and which lies at a distance of 5500 light years.

Telescopium Telescopii Tel *Telescope*
RA: 18 hr, Dec: −45°

A constellation which should, perhaps, have been more properly included with Corona Australis. It is surrounded by that constellation and Ara, Pavo, Indus and Sagittarius. The three brightest stars are all nestled on the border with Corona Australis. There is little here of observational interest.

Triangulum Trianguli Tri *Triangle*
RA: 02 hr, Dec: +35°

Triangulum is one of the earliest named constellations, despite being very inconspicuous. α Trianguli is only of mag 3·45 with β Trianguli of mag 3, which is again a departure from the correct sequence of decreasing magnitude for successive letter designations. The only object of note is the spiral galaxy M33, just visible to the naked eye under perfect conditions.

Taurus

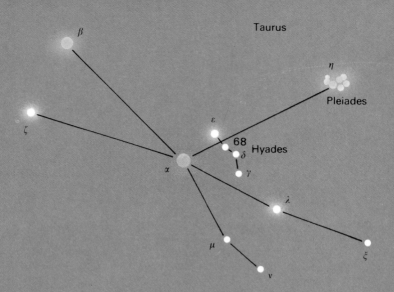

β

ζ

ε

68   Hyades

δ

γ

α

η

Pleiades

λ

μ

ν

ξ

Telescopium

α   ε

ζ

Triangulum

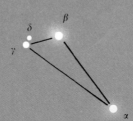

δ   β

γ

α

Triangulum Australe Trianguli Australis TrA
Southern Triangle
RA: 16 hr, Dec: −65°
Triangulum Australe is a Bayer constellation listed in his early 17th-century catalogue. It is fairly easily found from α Centauri.

Star α is a mag 1·93 K2 type with absolute mag −0·1 at a distance of 82 light years; star β is a F2 type of mag 2·87 at 42 light years distance; and star γ is of mag 2·94 being an A0 type of absolute mag 0·2 at a distance of 113 light years. Nothing else of note is found in this constellation.

Tucana Tucanae Tuc *Toucan*
RA: 23 hr, Dec: −60°
Tucana contains most of the Small Magellanic Cloud (SMC). This irregular galaxy is close to our own but lies at a rather greater distance than the Large Magellanic Cloud in Dorado. The constellation contains several interesting nebulae and two globular clusters of which the most prominent is 47 Tuc, close to the SMC. Star α is a mag 2·8, K3 type at a distance of 62 light years.

Ursa Major Ursae Majoris UMa *Great Bear*
RA: 11 hr, Dec: +50°
This is possibly the most famous of all the constellations because its seven main stars are very prominent and easily visible from the northern hemisphere. These seven stars, known as 'The Plough' or 'The Big Dipper', only form a small part of the whole constellation. It has a highly irregular outline and prominent stars are spread across a large area.

Taking the stars in sequence, and moving in increasing RA: α, Dubhe, is a mag 1·81, K0 close double with component mags of 1·88 and 4·82 and 107 light years away; star β, Merak, is a mag 2·37, A1 type with absolute mag 0·5 at a distance of 78 light years; γ, Phad, is an A0 type of mag 2·44 (absolute mag 0·2) 90 light years away; δ, Megrez, is a comparatively faint member at mag 3·3; ε, Alioth, is the brightest member of the seven at mag 1·79 with an A0 spectrum, absolute mag of 0·2 and it lies at a distance of 68 light years; star ζ, Mizar, is an A2 mag, 2·06 double with component mags of 2·3 and 4·0 and the former is itself a double − the first spectroscopic binary to be discovered; and finally, η, Alkaid, at the comparatively remote distance of 210 light years, is a B3 type of mag 1·87 (absolute mag −2·1).

Four interesting doubles are located in the constellation: star θ is actually a double with mag 3·19 and 14; star ι has mag 3·12 and 10·8 components; star χ has component mags of 4·0 and 4·2; and star o, Muscida, has components of mag 3·57 and 15. There are six

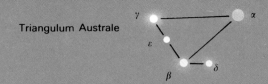

Triangulum Australe

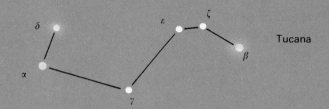

Tucana

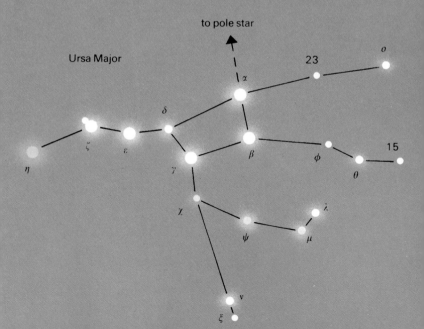

Ursa Major

to pole star

Messier objects in the constellation (M81, M82, M97, M101, M108 and M109). M97 is the mous planetary Owl Nebula, looking like a staring owl, with the remainder being galaxies in their own right.

Ursa Minor Ursae Minoris UMi *Little Bear*
RA: 15 hr, Dec: +75°

Ursa Minor was one of the originally named 48 constellations, and has the distinction of including the north celestial pole. Much of Ursa Minor seems nestled within the cradle of Draco but this constellation is unmistakably distinctive. Having found the star nearest to the celestial north pole the rest is easy to recognize.

The pole star itself, or the star which today is closest to the celestial north pole, is Polaris, α UMi, a mag 1·99–2·1 variable of F8 type and an absolute mag of −4·6. Lying at a distance of 680 light years, the star is attended by a mag 8·9 companion. Star β, Kochab, is a mag 2·04, K4 type and γ, Pherkad, is of mag 3·04. When Polaris, a notable Cepheid, is dim it is actually slightly fainter than the first of these stars.

Vela Velorum Vel *Sail (of a ship)*
RA: 09 hr, Dec: −50°

Vela is one of the three constellations formed from the original, and unwieldy, Argo Navis. It is bordered by Antila, Pyxis, Puppis, Carina and Centaurus. The designation of the various stars was set up when Vela was part of Argo Navis and the brightest star here is γ Velorum, a double with component mags of 2·2 and 4·8. Star δ, is a mag 1·95, A0 type with a mag 5·1 companion. A third companion to δ is actually a spectroscopic binary viewed as a single mag 10 star. The stars δ and κ, together with ι and ε in Carina, form the 'False Cross', sometimes mistaken for the constellation of Crux.

Ursa Minor

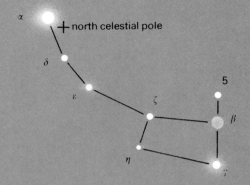

Vela

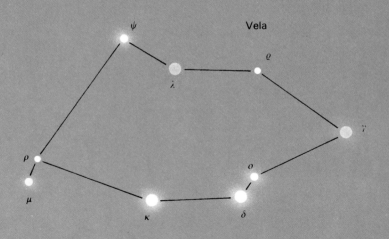

Virgo Virginis Vir *Virgin*
RA: 13 hr, Dec: 00°
Virgo is a zodiacal constellation and is second only to Hydra in area. The most prominent star in the constellation is α, Spica, southern-most of the seven brightest stars, with mag 0·91 and a location 220 light years from the Sun. The star is a variable, with a spectroscopic binary and appears as a hot white object. Star γ, of mag 2·5 and an absolute mag of 2·6 is a close binary. It lies at a distance of only 36 light years. Far to the west of the constellation lies β, Zavijava, of mag 3·8, and to the north ε, Vindemiatrix, is a mag 2·86 star of spectral type G9 with an absolute mag of 0·6 at a distance of 90 light years.

Virgo lies adjacent to Coma Berenices and the northern border of Virgo contains many interesting nebulae – all external galaxies. Most notable are M58, M59, M60, M84, M87, M89 and M90. On the southwestern border (with Corvus) the telescope will reveal the magnificent Sombrero Galaxy (M104). M49 and M61 lie between stars β and ε.

Volans Volantis Vol *Flying Fish*
RA: 08 hr, Dec: −70°
One of Bayer's constellations, Volans is more properly seen as an adjunct to Carina as it is most easily found from the stars β and ε Carinae. None of the stars in this region of the celestial sphere is of significance or as bright as mag 3. The keen-eyed observer may be able to discern the mag 9 companion to ζ and, far more easily, make out the K1 and G0 components of the double star γ.

Vulpecula Vulpeculae Vul *Little Fox*
RA: 20 hr, Dec: +25°
Vulpecula was one of the constellations named by Hevelius in 1690 and is situated alongside Sagitta but is probably best located from the star Albireo, β Cygni.

The constellation lies across part of the Milky Way, including an extension of the 'Great Rift' in Cygnus. The stars within Vulpecula are very faint and extremely inconspicuous and there is nothing of very great note in the constellation. The planetary nebula M27 (NGC 6853), widely known as the Dumbbell, can be found to the south, close to the border with Sagitta.

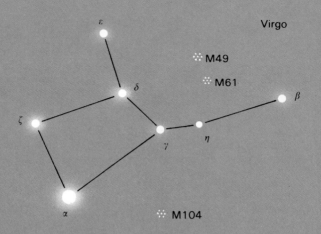

Virgo

ε

δ

ζ

γ η

β

α

M49

M61

M104

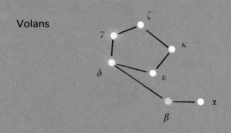

Volans

ζ

γ

κ

δ

ε

β α

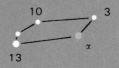

Vulpecula

10

3

13

α

Variable stars

One of the fields of observation, where the amateur can make a real contribution, is the study of variable stars. So many variable stars are now known that with limited time and restricted access to telescopes, most professional work must be confined to specific aspects of variability, and it is often only amateurs who can follow stars' changes over a long period. Even so, the vast majority of individual variables go unstudied.

Some of the brightest stars are variable and can be followed by the naked eye. Most of them have fairly small amplitudes which can be difficult to determine accurately. With binoculars, however, many thousands of stars are available for study, and the numbers rise with increased apertures, so no observer can hope to cover more than a small fraction of the known objects.

There are so many different classes of variable stars that they cannot all be described here. However, the most popular are the long-period variables (periods over 100 days and reasonably regular light-curves), the semi-regulars (more erratic behaviour but still with some periodicity), and the eruptive stars, particularly the dwarf novae (sudden outbursts with 'periods' of between a few tens of days to years, depending upon the individual stars) as well as other related types. Of the other classes the most important are probably the eclipsing binaries, where the orbital plane of the two individuals is aligned so that each star periodically eclipses the other.

The system of nomenclature used for variable stars is a little complicated. The majority are known by single or double letters, e.g. R Scuti or WW Aurigae, or by a number preceded by the letter V, e.g. V1500 Cygni, which is the official name for Nova Cygni 1975. The positions and characteristics of many of the brighter variable stars are listed in celestial handbooks and shown on many charts and atlases. Detailed charts of individual fields can be obtained from the organizations that specialize in variable star observation, together with magnitude sequences of comparison stars. As the magnitude of a variable is usually obtained by comparing its brightness with two non-variable comparison stars, one slightly brighter and the other slightly fainter than the variable, it is important that these 'official' magnitude sequences are used, as magnitudes derived from other (or mixed) sources may not be consistent with one another. The number of observations which are made of a particular object will depend upon the actual class of object. Slow variables should only be observed about once every ten days, whereas eruptive objects can be estimated perhaps every hour when they are caught on the rise to maximum. Although a light-curve may be constructed from observations by an individual observer, there are inevitable personal errors. For this reason it is usual for observations to be reported to one of the amateur groups – just as with many other types of observation – which then prepare mean light-curves using many other estimates, and also carry out further analyses. They may then pass the observations to professional workers for further detailed analysis. The professionals, in their turn, may request specific coverage of particular objects, perhaps to coincide with periods of observation by other specialized telescopes or satellites operating in any of the many regions of the electromagnetic spectrum.

Many amateurs now use photoelectric equipment, and this can have many uses in the study of variable stars, not least in the determination of accurate sequences of magnitudes for objects to be studied by other means. In addition, such equipment may be used to detect both low-amplitude and short-term variations which are difficult, if not impossible, to follow by other methods. All sorts

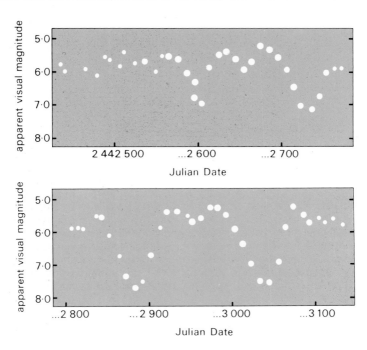

Fig. 25 A light curve of R Scuti, based on observations for 1975 and 1976.

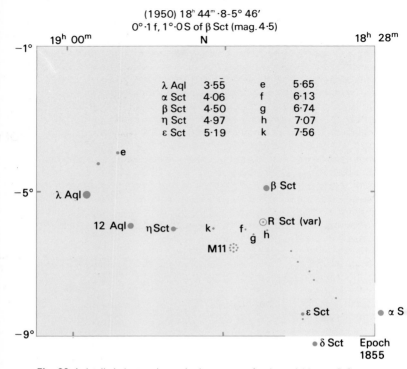

λ Aql	3·55	e	5·65
α Sct	4·06	f	6·13
β Sct	4·50	g	6·74
η Sct	4·97	h	7·07
ε Sct	5·19	k	7·56

Fig. 26 A detailed chart and magnitude sequence for the variable star R Scuti, which may conveniently be observed during the evening in late summer to early autumn. Magnitude estimates made at intervals of a week or so should show the star's variation.

of classes come within this category, including RR Lyrae variables.

In the field of eclipsing binaries, photoelectric work, especially when combined with professional spectroscopic determinations, can provide a wealth of data about the stars. This includes information about their absolute sizes, masses, orbits, limb darkening and so on.

Quite apart from the derivation of light-curves, the actual discovery of certain types of variables is very important, and many amateurs carry out visual or photographic patrols aimed at the detection of novae and supernovae both in our galaxy and in other galaxies. An example of this could be the early observations made by amateurs of the Supernova of February 1987 in the large Magellanic Cloud.

Although many variables are discovered by photography, the method is not widely used to follow brightness changes, partly because of the time (and expense) involved, and also because of the problems of the different response of films to that of the human eye – although allowance for this may be made without too much difficulty. However, photography does have the great advantage over other available techniques that several variables may be recorded on one exposure, and frequently nova patrol photographs are used to derive the magnitudes of objects in their fields. These can form an extremely useful supplement to visual observations of the same objects.

Apart from telling us more about how stars work and evolve, what other use can observations of variable stars be put to? They can help us to measure the size of the universe, by allowing astronomers to determine the distance to nearby galaxies.

A most interesting class of stars, known as Cepheid variables, significantly assist measurements of star distances by relating absolute magnitudes to periodic variations in brightness. These stars fluctuate between fixed levels of maximum and minimum brightness in precise relation to absolute magnitude; the brighter the star, the longer the period of oscillation. For example, consider a cluster of stars containing some Cepheid variables. We can assume that the stars are all at pretty much the same distance from the solar system, by virtue of the fact that they are in a cluster. Careful measurement of the periods of the Cepheids would determine the absolute magnitude of each one. By comparing this known luminosity value with the light received on the Earth, which is known as the apparent magnitude, it would be possible to calculate how much light had been lost due to the inverse square law. This would then reveal how far the light had travelled through space and, consequently, the distance of the cluster from the observer.

The first variable of this type to be observed was δ Cephei, in the constellation Cepheus (see page 64). Since then, many Cepheids have been observed in regions of our own as well as other galaxies, and their accurate measurement has refined the astronomer's knowledge of distances in the universe. Henrietta Leavitt first brought Cepheids to fame in 1911 and for more than 40 years these stars (later known as Population II Cepheids) in the nearest galaxy comparable to our own, M31 in Andromeda, were used to obtain a distance estimate of 800,000 light years. This changed to 2.2 million light years when a more luminous class (known as Population I Cepheids) was discovered by Walter Baade in 1952.

Some telescopic variables

Name	RA hr	min.	Dec deg	min	Magnitude range		Period (days)	Remarks
R Andromedae	00	22	+38	18	6.1	14.9	409	
W Andromedae	02	14	+44	04	6.7	14.5	397	
R Aquilae	19	04	+08	09	5.7	12.0	300	
R Aurigae	05	13	+53	32	6.7	13.7	459	
R Bootis	14	35	+26	57	6.7	12.8	223	
R Cassiopeiae	23	56	+51	06	5.5	13.0	431	
T Centauri	13	38	−33	21	5.5	9.0	91	Semi-regular
R Coronae Borealis	15	46	+28	18	5.8	14.8		Irregular
W Cygni	21	34	+45	09	5.0	7.6	131	
SS Cygni	21	41	+43	21	8.2	12.1		Irregular
U Geminorum	07	52	+22	08	8.8	14.4		Irregular
X Leonis	09	48	+12	07	12.0	15.1		Irregular
R Leporis	04	57	−14	53	5.9	10.5	432	
R Sculptoris	01	24	−32	48	5.8	7.7	363	Semi-regular
R Scuti	18	45	−05	46	5.0	8.4	144	

Double and multiple stars

Double and multiple star systems present many striking colour and magnitude contrasts. Many amateurs derive great satisfaction from seeking out and examining different systems. Close binaries are excellent for testing both a telescope's resolution and an observer's eyesight, so this aspect also presents a real challenge.

Resolution is dependent upon the aperture of the equipment being used, but refractors usually resolve closer pairs than reflectors of the same aperture. Some interesting systems are listed in the table on page 117, with a note on some which are suitable for telescopic resolution tests.

For the purposes of resolution tests, apparent doubles – where the stars merely happen to lie on the same line of sight, and the separation remains constant apart from any proper motion – are better objects than the true binaries, where the stars are in orbit about one another.

The study of true binaries is rather neglected by both amateur and professional astronomers, but it remains very worthwhile, partly because of this neglect. Very frequently the separations of the components of binaries and multiples are quite inaccurately quoted in textbooks, largely because many years have elapsed since the last measurements were made. The orbital motion of the stars may have converted 'easy' systems into very difficult objects, and vice versa. Even a single measurement is therefore of interest, but a series on a single object, perhaps continued over years, is of great value. If a proper orbit can be defined the orbital period and also the relative masses of the components can be found.

Generally refractors are favoured for this work, with large aperture and long focal length being great advantages. Although professional astronomers employ very sophisticated techniques, amateurs use one of the many forms of visual micrometer, the bifilar type being one of the best and perhaps the most readily understood and used. The measurements required are those of position angle (PA) and separation. Because of the problems encountered, most especially with close binaries and those with very unequal magnitude components, it is usual for a set of PA and separation estimates to be made at any one time, the most probable values being then derived mathematically. From these, the apparent orbits may be plotted, either by continuing a series of observations over a period of years, or by combining modern measurements with those of earlier observers. The calculations required for deriving the full orbital elements and relative masses of the components are fairly complex, and are usually only applied to observations of a sufficiently high accuracy. However, such studies are of great importance in the investigation of stellar characteristics and there are indications that this is now being recognized, and that more amateurs are turning to the measurement of double and multiple stars as a primary interest.

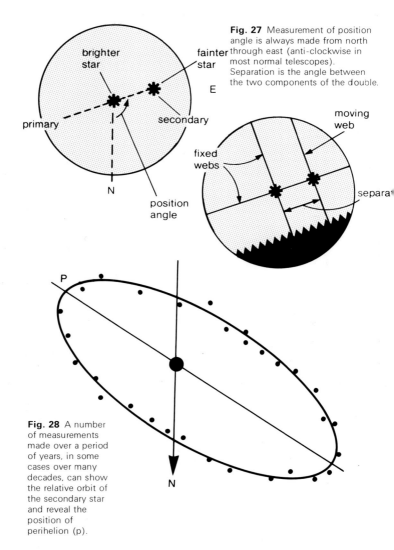

Fig. 27 Measurement of position angle is always made from north through east (anti-clockwise in most normal telescopes). Separation is the angle between the two components of the double.

Fig. 28 A number of measurements made over a period of years, in some cases over many decades, can show the relative orbit of the secondary star and reveal the position of perihelion (p).

Double Stars

The following list gives 20 of the easier double stars that you might like to try observing.
You can find them in any good star atlas.

Name	Visual magnitudes	Separation (arc sec)	Position (degrees)	Remarks
γ Andromedae	3.0 5.0	9.4	64	Yellow, blue
γ Arii̇s	4.2 4.4	7.8	0	Easy
δ Boötis	3.2 7.4	105.0	79	Fixed
ι Cancri	4.4 6.5	31.0	307	Yellow, blue; easy
α Capricorni	3.3 4.2	376.0	291	Naked-eye pair
η Cassiopeiae	3.7 7.4	12.2	310	Cream, blue; easy
β Cephei	3.3 8.0	14.0	250	Easy with a three inch
δ Cephei	var 7.5	41.0	192	Very easy
α Centauri	0.0 1.7	21.7	212	Very easy
α Crucis	1.6 2.1	4.7	114	—
γ Crucis	1.6 6.7	111.0	212	Wide optical pair
β Cygni	3.0 5.3	34.3	55	Yellow, blue; beautiful
α Lyrae	0.0 10.5	73.0	180	Optical double
ε Lyrae	{ 4.6 6.3	{ 2.6	{ 356	Double-double
	{ 4.9 5.2	{ 2.2	{ 93	
β Orionis	0.1 6.7	9.5	205	—
θ Orionis	{ 6.8 7.9	{ 8.7	{ 32	Trapezium in M42
	{ 6.8 5.4	{ 13.4	{ 241	
α Scorpii	0.9 6.8	3.0	275	Red, green
υ Scorpii	4.2 6.5	42.0	336	—
α Tauri	0.8 11.2	131.0	32	Faint secondary
ζ Ursae Majoris	2.1 4.2	14.4	151	Naked-eye pair
				Very easy

Tracking artificial satellites

Observations of artificial satellites can be used to provide information about two aspects of the Earth. They are affected by any
irregularities in the Earth's gravitational field, and precise determination of their orbits has resulted in a most detailed knowledge of
gravitational variations from place to place. Studies of the motion of
natural satellites has given information about the gravitational
fields of other planets. However, this knowledge has been greatly
increased in those cases where spacecraft have passed close by, or
even better, orbited the body. Information can also be gained about

Fig. 29 One of the earlier and brighter artificial satellites, Echo 1, is shown in this
photograph taken looking towards the galactic centre.

the upper atmosphere, especially its density. Satellite orbits are greatly affected by the density of the regions through which they are passing, particularly at perigee. By heating and expansion of the upper layers of the atmosphere, solar flares greatly increase the density and thus have a marked effect on satellite orbits. Such changes can precipitate orbital decay and re-entry into the atmosphere. This phenomenon becomes particularly noticeable around the times of maximum solar activity, about every eleven years (see page 15). Satellites in lower orbits are affected the most. Indeed it was this increased solar activity in the mid 1970's, and its subsequent effects on the Earth's atmosphere, that caused the earlier than expected demise of the abandoned Skylab space station. With no operational propulsion systems on board, controllers were unable to manoeuvre the vehicle into a higher orbit. The large cross-section of the station caused a lot of atmospheric drag, which subsequently slowed it until its orbit decayed catastrophically. Skylab met its firey end over the deserts of Western Australia.

All that is required for these studies is a number of accurate positional determinations at known times. This is more easily said than done, but although special large cameras are used by professional teams, visual observations can yield the required degree of accuracy. Timing usually presents few problems, and stop watches or the simultaneous recording of radio or telephone time signals and the observer's event markers are quite suitable.

Position measurement is more difficult and the precise means adopted will depend upon the equipment employed. The purpose is to obtain a satellite's right ascension and declination at a determined instant. Some instruments, such as theodolites, will give readings in altitude and azimuth, and these will be converted into RA and Dec when analysed.

In the early days of artificial satellite studies, teams of observers used 'fixed' telescopes to establish a grid of overlapping fields in the sky. It was then possible for the particular observer (or observers) who saw the satellite to obtain the time of its transit across a crosswire in the field. Now it is common to find individual observers with binoculars or similar small-aperture equipment. The method consists of observing the satellite's path against the stellar background, and of choosing a pair of suitable reference stars and noting its position relative to them at a certain instant. The stars chosen should be readily identifiable, and given in a good atlas and catalogue. Bright objects should be chosen whenever possible. More than one observation should be obtained during the satellite's pass, but this may not be practicable on some occasions as the satellite may run into eclipse. From the positions and times (and

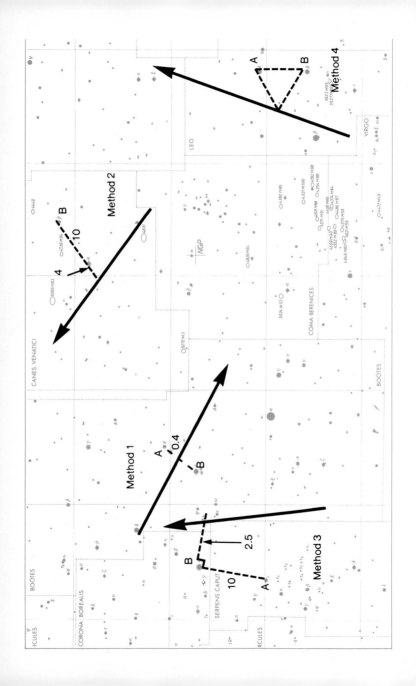

additional information such as the observer's exact latitude, longitude and altitude) the orbit may be derived.

With so many objects in orbit, it is essential that the proper identity of the satellites should be known. It is normal to prepare 'Look Data' predictions giving information on where individual satellites may be seen. Some observers prepare such predictions for themselves, but normally a national centre does this.

Magnitude observations are also of great interest and may be made by methods similar to those used for variable stars. Satellites, rockets and debris are of all shapes, sizes and reflective properties, as well as being at various distances from the Earth, so a whole range of magnitudes is encountered, with only the brightest being visible to the naked eye. Although satellites move more slowly than meteors they also suffer from the same effect that moving objects must be rather brighter than fixed ones for them to be perceived by the eye. This factor, as well as the aperture of the optical equipment, must be taken into account when choosing objects to observe.

If tumbling accidentally, or having been set spinning deliberately, satellites also show regular magnitude variations, while large reflective surfaces such as solar panels can give rise to bright flashes visible from the ground. All these useful pieces of information should be recorded by the observer. Quite apart from the magnitude variations mentioned, all objects will fade as they enter the Earth's penumbra, or disappear completely within the umbral cone.

Satellite re-entries can be very bright, and on occasions can exceed the brightness of the full Moon. Some are thus visible in daylight, when it will usually be necessary to record the track in terms of altitude and azimuth rather than in celestial coordinates. If a bright re-entry is expected, it may be possible to photograph it deliberately. A spectacular example was the re-entry of the US Skylab Space Station in July 1979. Brilliant flashes were seen over Western Australia as the space station came down.

Although some very experienced observers may use large telescopes and specialized techniques to provide an exceptionally high degree of accuracy, the observation of artificial satellites is yet another example of how amateur observation with comparatively simple techniques and equipment can give results of great scientific value.

Fig. 30 Satellite observation consists of estimating the position in terms of the distance between suitable stars (such as those marked A and B on this chart), by one or other of the methods shown here, whichever is most appropriate at the time.

Table 1. The 20 brightest stars

Star name		Apparent mag.
α Eridani	Achernar	+0.48
α Tauri	Aldebaran	+0.85
α Aurigae	Capella	+0.08
β Orionis	Rigel	+0.11
α Orionis	Betelgeuse	(+0.4 to +1.3)
α Carinae	Canopus	−0.73
α Canis Majoris	Sirius	−1.45
α Canis Minoris	Procyon	+0.35
β Geminorum	Pollux	+1.15
α Crucis	Acrux	+0.9
β Crucis	Mimosa	+1.26
α Virginis	Spica	+0.96
β Centauri	Agena	+0.6
α Boötis	Arcturus	−0.06
α Centauri	Rigel Kent	−0.27
α Scorpii	Antares	+0.9
α Lyrae	Vega	+0.04
α Aquilae	Altair	+0.77
α Cygni	Deneb	+1.35
α Pisces Austrini	Fomalhaut	+1.16

Table 2. Planetary data

	Mercury	Venus	Earth
Mean distance from Sun (million km)	57.9	108.2	149.6
Mean distance from Sun (Au)	0.39	0.72	1.0
Period of revolution	88 days	224.7 days	365.3 days
Eccentricity of orbit	0.206	0.007	0.017
Inclination of orbit	7°	3.4°	0°
Inclination of axis	<28°	3°	23.45°
Rotation period	59 days	−243 days	23 h 56 min
Orbital velocity (km/s)	47.9	35	29.8
Diameter at equator (km)	4880	12,104	12,756
Oblateness	0	0	0.003
Density (g/cm³)	5.4	5.2	5.5
Volume (×Earth)	0.06	0.88	1
Mass (×Earth)	0.055	0.815	1
Atmospheric pressure (bars)	10^{-6}	90	1
Satellites (discovered)	—	—	1

Absolute mag.	RA hr	min.	Dec degrees	min.	Spectral type
− 2.2	01	37.3	−57	17	B5
− 0.7	04	35.9	+16	30	K5
− 0.6	05	15.8	+45	59	G8
− 7.0	05	14.5	−08	12	B8
− 5.9 av	05	55.0	+07	24	M2
+ 0.2	06	23.9	−52	42	F0
+ 1.4	06	44.6	−16	42	A1
+ 2.7	07	38.7	+05	15	F5
+ 0.9	07	44.6	+28	04	K0
− 3.5	12	26.0	−63	03	B2
− 4.7	12	47.0	−59	37	B0
− 3.4	13	24.6	−11	06	B1
− 5.0	14	03.0	−60	19	B1
− 0.2	14	15.1	+19	14	K2
+ 4.3	14	39.0	−60	47	G2
− 4.7	16	28.5	−26	25	M1
+ 0.5	18	36.9	+38	47	A0
+ 2.3	19	50.1	+38	46	A7
− 7.3	20	41.0	+45	14	A2
+ 0.08	22	57.0	−29	41	A3

Mars	Jupiter	Saturn	Uranus	Neptune	Pluto
227.9	778.3	1429.4	2875.0	4504.4	5900
1.52	5.20	9.55	19.21	30.11	39.44
687 days	11.86 y	29.46 y	84.01 y	164.8 y	247.7 y
0.093	0.048	0.056	0.047	0.009	0.25
1.9°	1.3°	2.5°	0.8°	1.8°	17.2°
25.20°	3.08°	26.73°	82.8°	28.8°	—
24 h 37 min	9 h 50 min	10 h 14 min	−11 h	16 h	6 days 9 h
24.1	13.1	9.6	6.8	5.4	4.7
6794	142,800	120,000	51,800	48,600	3000
0.005	0.06	0.1	0.06	0.02	—
3.9	1.3	0.7	1.3	1.7	1.3
0.15	1316	755	67	57	0.1
0.107	317.9	95.2	14.6	17.2	0.002
0.06	—	—	—	—	—
2	16	17	15	2	1

Table 3. Greek alphabet

Alpha	A α	Iota	I ι	Rho	P ρ
Beta	B β	Kappa	K κ	Sigma	Σ σ
Gamma	Γ γ	Lambda	Λ λ	Tau	T τ
Delta	Δ δ	Mu	M μ	Upsilon	Y υ
Epsilon	E ε	Nu	N υ	Phi	Φ φ
Zeta	Z ζ	Xi	Ξ ζ	Chi	X x
Eta	H η	Omicron	O o	Psi	Ψ ψ
Theta	Θ θ	Pi	Π π	Omega	Ω ω

Further reading

Couper, H. & Henbest, N., *The Planets*, Pan Books, London, 1985.

Couper, H. & Henbest, N., *The Stars*, Pan Books, London, 1988.

Ferris, T., *Galaxies*, Stewart, Tabori & Chang, New York, 1980.

Henbest, N. & Marten, M., *The New Astronomy*, Cambridge University Press, Cambridge, 1980.

Kelley, K., *The Home Planet*, Addison-Wesley, Reading, Mass., 1988.

Newton, J. & Teece, P., *The Cambridge Deep-Sky Album*, Cambridge University Press, Cambridge, 1983.

Ronan, C. (ed.), *Amateur Astronomy*, 2nd edn, Hamlyn, London, 1989.

Sagan, C., *Cosmos*, Macdonald, London, 1981.

Tirion, W., *Sky Atlas 2000*, Sky Publishing Corporation, Cambridge, Mass., 1981.

There are aways a good selection of both general and specialist astronomy articles in *Sky & Telescope* (Sky Publishing Corp.) and *Astronomy* (Astromedia Corp.). Both of these magazines are published monthly.

Your local public library will be able to help you find other books to suit your interests. They may also be able to tell you if there is an amateur astronomy club or society in your area. It is certainly worth joining one if you have anything more than a passing interest in astronomy.

Index

127